Expeditions
in Reading

4

K12 Summit
CURRICULUM

Book Staff and Contributors

Kristen Kinney-Haines   *Director, English Language Arts*
Amy Rauen   *Director, Instructional Design*
Charlotte Fullerton   *Senior Media Editor*
Mary Beck Desmond   *Senior Text Editor*
Tricia Battipede   *Senior Creative Manager, Cover Design*
Caitlin Gildrien   *Print Visual Designer, Cover Design*
Tim Mansfield   *Writer*
DoubleInk Publishing Services   *Print Visual Design*

About K12 Inc.

K12 Inc. (NYSE: LRN) drives innovation and advances the quality of education by delivering state-of-the-art digital learning platforms and technology to students and school districts around the world. K12 is a company of educators offering its online and blended curriculum to charter schools, public school districts, private schools, and directly to families. More information can be found at K12.com.

Illustrations Credits

All illustrations © K12 unless otherwise noted
9, 13, 16 Alessia Girasole. **21, 22, 24** Jimmy Holder. **28, 31** Sergio DeGiorgi. **86–87, 88** Merrilee Liddiard. **91, 95, 104, 110, 116** Juan Manuel Moreno. **120, 123** Olga & Aleksey Ivanov. **125, 127, 130** Oriol Vidal. **134–135** Jennifer Bricking. **167, 170** Kristen Sorra. **177, 184, 189** Angeles Ruiz. **191, 199** C.B. Canga. **202–203, 209, 213** Marionna Cabassa.

Photo Credits

Front Cover   Landscape © ubrx/iStock; Birds © seamartini/iStock
Title Page   Birds © seamartini/iStock
Cover and Interior Pattern   Spiral © Silmen/iStock
35 Project Mercury astronaut John Glenn © Ralph Morse/The LIFE Picture Collection/Getty Images. **39** Parade © Dean Conger/Corbis via Getty Images. **41** John Glenn speaking NASA Photo/Alamy Stock Photo. **43** Glenn entering Friendship 7 capsule NASA. **50** Wilbur Wright © Ipsumpix/Corbis via Getty Images; Orville Wright © Ipsumpix/Corbis via Getty Images. **51** Wright Flyer © SSPL/Getty Images. **54** Wright Brothers Flight at Kitty Hawk by Paul Carey © Bridgeman Images. **56** Wilbur and Orville Wright NASA. **59** Bessie Coleman © George Rinhart/Getty Images. **62** Bessie Coleman © Michael Ochs Archives/Getty Images. **64** Bessie Coleman © neftali/Shutterstock. **69** Charles Lindbergh © Archive Pics/Alamy Stock Photo. **71** Charles Lindbergh © Science Source/Getty Images. **74** Charles Lindbergh sitting in the cockpit of his plane the Spirit of St Louis before takeoff © Bettmann/Getty Images. Spirit of St Louis via Paris © Sueddeutsche Zeitung Photo/Alamy Stock Photo. **80–81** Park © mikolajn/iStock. **82-83** Blocks © Thanat Jirapongsit/iStock. **85** Girl © Tom Kelley Archive/iStock. **143** Books © Piotr Wytrazek/iStock. **146** Elizabeth Blackwell © Museum of the City of New York/Getty Images; Gold frame © Boris25/iStock. **153** Pasteur animal testing © Beeldbewerking/Getty Images. **154** Louis Pasteur © DEA Picture Library/Getty Images. **157** Laboratory instruments used by Louis Pasteur © Photo 12/Getty Images. **162** Coral reef © Reinhard Dirscherl/Alamy Stock Photo.

Printed by Walsworth, Marceline, MO, USA, April 2019

Expeditions
in Reading

K12 Summit
CURRICULUM

Table of Contents

Cinderella Around the World

Cinderella

Once upon a time, in a country village there lived a lovely young maiden. This maiden was gentle and kindhearted. She had lived a happy and comfortable life with her loving mother and father in their own grand estate until the untimely death of her mother. Her father soon looked for a new woman to marry so that his daughter would once again have a mother.

The maiden's father met a widow who was raising two daughters of her own. Her daughters were similar in age to his daughter. The widow and her daughters seemed kind, so the two soon married. Then the woman and her two daughters moved in. Sadly, the new mother and her daughters were actually not kind. They pretended to be nice whenever the father was around. But when his daughter was left alone with her new family members, they treated her poorly. They made her do all the chores and wait on them like a servant.

"Do the mending!" yelled her stepmother.

"Sweep the steps!" yelled her stepsister.

"Where is our food!?!" yelled her other stepsister.

The demands and requests went on all day long, every day. The daughter could barely keep up. She never could find time to talk to her father about her problems. The stepsisters had taken over her bedroom and forced her to sleep in the kitchen. Every night she would curl up near the fire trying to keep warm. This caused the girl to often have smudges of soot on her face and clothing, so the stepsisters and their mother then began to call her Cinderella, since she always wore evidence of **cinders** from the fire. This became their new name for her.

"Cinderella why have you not yet done the washing?" yelled her stepmother.

cinders ashes from a fire

"Cinderella don't just stand there! I need my ribbons tied in my hair NOW!" yelled her stepsister.

"Cinderella why have you not brought me my tea? I asked you ten minutes ago!" yelled her other stepsister.

Cinderella rarely saw her father now. He did not realize that things were so terrible for her because his new wife and daughters always behaved sweetly toward Cinderella whenever he was around. He also did not think it was odd to see his daughter always wearing a plain gown with an apron and cinder smudges because she had always loved to cook. His first wife had been a wonderful cook. She had spent time in the kitchen every day with their daughter. He thought his daughter was spending time in the kitchen as a way to remember her mother.

Then one evening there was a visitor at the door. It was a messenger from the palace! He handed Cinderella an invitation to a royal ball! It was addressed to "every eligible young maiden." She was an eligible young maiden. That meant she was invited to the ball too! As she was trying to read the rest of the invitation, it was suddenly grabbed from her hands.

Her stepmother had been the one to snatch the invitation. As she read it aloud to her daughters, a huge smile grew on her face.

"Girls, this is your chance! The prince is throwing a ball and every eligible maiden in the kingdom is invited. He will be looking for his future bride at this ball. We have lots of planning to do. You must not fail me!" the stepmother explained.

Cinderella smiled and said, "How lovely, we can all go to a ball!"

"YOU go to the ball?" her stepsisters exclaimed as they laughed and laughed.

"It does say EVERY eligible maiden. I AM an eligible maiden." Cinderella responded.

"You do have a point Cinderella," Her stepmother replied. "All right, you may go to the ball, too, Cinderella. As long as you finish all your chores. Oh, and you will have to find something nice to wear."

Cinderella thanked her stepmother and hurried off to do her chores. As the day went on her stepsisters kept creating more chores for her to do. They seemed to be making messes on purpose. Still, Cinderella was hopeful. Her mother had always told her that good things come from hard work. Cinderella knew that if she kept working hard she could finish on time.

It was nightfall when Cinderella finally finished. After helping her stepsisters get dressed, she rushed to the kitchen. She cleaned her face and hands. Then she opened a trunk of her mother's old clothes and pulled out a lovely gown. Just then her stepmother entered the room. She told Cinderella that she was too late. The carriage was already here and they were leaving without her.

Cinderella was heartbroken. She laid her head on the gown on top of the trunk and began to cry. Cinderella's father walked in and saw her crying on her mother's gown. He placed a hand on her back. Cinderella looked up with tears in her eyes. She was about to tell him what happened when he spoke instead.

"I know you miss your mother. I miss her too. I understand how sad you are. You do not have to go to the ball," he said as he kissed her on the cheek and walked out the door.

Cinderella had never felt so lonely in all her life! She ran out back to her mother's grave near the garden. She lay down on the grave and began to sob. Suddenly, she saw a bright light coming from the trees. She looked up and saw a beautiful woman. She was dressed in a sparkling gown and she had a shining wand. She told Cinderella that she was her fairy godmother. She said she had been sent by Cinderella's mother to help her.

With a wave of her wand, the fairy godmother transformed Cinderella's rags into a beautiful ball gown! Cinderella looked down and saw two perfect glass slippers

on her feet. Another wave of the wand and Cinderella's hair was swirled up and held with jewels. Next her fairy godmother turned a pumpkin into a carriage. She also turned some mice into horses. And a rat into a coachman and lizards into footmen!

The fairy godmother helped Cinderella into the carriage. Then she told her that all of this magic would only last until midnight. Cinderella smiled and nodded and thanked her fairy godmother, and then she was off to the ball.

Cinderella's carriage was the last to arrive. As she walked up the steps alone, she saw the prince. He was far ahead, greeting a long line of maidens one by one. As Cinderella entered the ball, all eyes were on her. No one else had ever seen a gown and hairstyle like hers. All were admiring her beauty. The prince stopped what he was doing to stare at Cinderella in awe. She blushed and walked away from the line toward the door to the garden.

Cinderella strolled through the garden, admiring its loveliness. She heard a man's voice behind a rosebush in front of her. He asked her how she was enjoying the party. She thanked him for asking and told him she was having a fine time so far. Then she admitted to being a bit nervous and unsure of herself. She told him she had never been to a ball. He asked her to dance with him right there in the garden.

She agreed as he stepped from behind the bush. It was the prince! Cinderella's cheeks turned pink. She looked down as he grabbed her hand. They began to dance and it felt so natural. They talked as they danced. He was so kind and so interested in all she had to say. They talked and danced. They danced and they talked. It felt like they had known each other forever even though they had only just met.

Cinderella was wishing she never had to leave. Then she heard the clock begin to strike. It was nearly midnight! The magic would stop and she would be back in rags! She thanked the prince for a lovely time but told him she really must be going. He begged her to stay and started to follow her as she hurried toward the steps.

As she rushed down the steps, one of her glass slippers fell off, but she kept going. The prince stopped to grab the slipper and just at that moment the magic ended and Cinderella was in rags. She jumped over the staircase to hide. On the ground she saw that the other glass slipper had not disappeared. She put it in her apron pocket and quickly went on her way. Once home, she rushed into the kitchen and hid the slipper in her mother's old trunk of clothes.

The next morning there was a guest at the door. He said he was there to try a glass slipper on every young maiden who had attended last night's ball and that the prince would marry the maiden who is the owner of this slipper.

Cinderella could not believe what she was hearing. Good things were finally happening to her!

While her stepsisters fought over who would be first to try on the slipper, Cinderella went to the kitchen. She got the other glass slipper from the trunk. She entered the room and showed it to the guest. Her stepsisters and stepmother were in shock! They could not believe that Cinderella had been the mysterious beautiful maiden from the ball.

Cinderella was escorted to the palace to her prince. She brought her father with her, and on the way she explained to him how cruel her stepmother and stepsisters really were. Her father decided to leave them forever and come live in the palace with his daughter.

And as for Cinderella, she and the prince were married, of course, and they lived happily ever after.

Mystery!

The Mystery of the Missing Hamburger

It was seven on Saturday morning. I was asleep because, well, it was seven on Saturday morning. The phone rang, and I wanted to ignore it, but something told me not to. That something was Mom, who always wakes up before dawn. She was in the den, exercising to a fitness show on TV.

"Answer that, Juan! I'm just getting a good sweat going!" she said.

I picked up the phone. The girl on the line sounded upset. She said she needed my help. I jotted down her address in a notebook I keep by the phone and said I'd be there in twenty minutes.

When I entered the den, I was dressed: khakis and a striped shirt. Mom was jogging in place as the man on TV said to keep those knees up. She did have a good sweat going, and she was keeping those knees up. I told her I had a case and asked if she'd seen my magnifying glass.

"Drawer," Mom said between breaths, her legs pumping like a pair of pistons. "Do you really use that?"

"I'm a detective," I said, taking the magnifying glass from the drawer.

"Yes, sweetie, but do you need the magnifying glass?"

"Sometimes," I answered. "Plus, it makes me feel authentic, especially since you won't buy me an awesome double-billed hat."

"Those cost a lot of money!" she said, her face red from exercising and the fact that we've had this argument about double-billed hats before.

I said I knew, told her to enjoy her workout, and left. I should have had breakfast, but I was eager to get cracking. In my experience, the more time passes, the harder it is to solve a mystery. I **despise** an unsolved mystery.

My client was Veronica Weiss. She lived in an apartment two blocks away. I knocked once on her front door and she opened it so quickly that my second knock nearly ended with my punching her in the nose. She was as eager as I was to solve this case.

"Juan Lopez, private detective," I said, and she invited me in.

Veronica wore green sweatpants and a green T-shirt. There was also a green bow in her red hair. She looked like a **leprechaun**, but I didn't say that because it doesn't

-----

despise to dislike, scorn, or look down upon with contempt
leprechaun an elflike character of Irish folklore

pay to insult clients. She showed me to the scene of the crime: her living room.

"So someone stole your hamburger," I said. "When did you last see it?"

"Before bed, I put it there," she said, pointing to a side table between a chair and the cage that housed her parrot, Squawk. "It was on that plate, all set for me to eat this morning."

There was a note near the empty plate on the side table. In green ink, it read, *"Property of Veronica,"* and the rest of the paper was covered in green hearts.

"Green is your favorite color," I said.

"How'd you know?" she asked.

"I'm a detective," I said. "You were gonna eat the hamburger this morning. Why not last night?"

"Because cold breakfast burgers are great," she replied. "My brother, Vinnie, and I love them."

I grabbed my notebook and **examined** the plate. I even used my magnifying glass. Where the hamburger had been there were now only some sesame seeds. I took some notes.

"Sesame seed bun?" I asked.

"Yes. No ketchup. No cheese. No pickles," she said.

"Cold, plain hamburgers for breakfast. You're a pretty strange bird, Veronica," I said.

....

examined studied or looked at carefully

"Pretty bird!" said Squawk from his cage.

I didn't know the bird could talk. It made me jump. Veronica apologized and explained that she'd taught Squawk to speak.

"What can he say?" I asked.

"'Hello' and 'goodbye.' And he says 'All done' after he eats," she explained. "But that's the first time he's talked today. I think he's upset about my hamburger, too. He hasn't touched his birdseed."

I nodded and asked if her brother was around. He was in his bedroom reading. I followed Veronica down the hall.

"Is Vinnie a **suspect**?" she asked.

"Everyone is a suspect," I said as she opened the bedroom door.

Vinnie was two years older than me, and he was deaf. When he saw us, he put down his book and **feverishly** signed at Veronica. She signed back just as quickly. It was clear they were arguing, probably about our coming into his room uninvited. When they both cooled off, I asked Veronica to sign some questions to Vinnie.

....

suspect one thought by the authorities to perhaps have caused a crime
feverishly actively or with strong emotion

"Have you seen Veronica's hamburger?" I asked. "Is it possible that you ate her breakfast burger?"

As Veronica signed, Vinnie looked annoyed. He reached down and picked up a plate from the floor next to him. A half-eaten burger sat on it. He signed again. Veronica **translated**.

"He says he'd never eat one of my plain, dry, boring burgers. He thinks a breakfast burger needs ketchup, cheese, and pickles. Like his."

Again, Vinnie motioned to his burger. I thanked him, and we left his room. In the hall, Veronica looked **distraught**.

"Can you solve the case?" she asked.

"I think I already have," I said. "Come on."

We returned to the living room. I examined the bottom of Squawk's cage. Then I looked at the tube of bird feed hanging from its side. I picked up the burger-less plate and held it near Squawk.

"All done!" the parrot said loudly, confirming my hunch.

"There's your culprit," I told Veronica as I put the plate down.

"Squawk?!" she asked, stunned. "How?"

"The plate was close enough for him to grab the

....

translated related, or expressed the sense of, words from one language to another
distraught very worried or upset

burger with his beak. He hasn't eaten this morning because he's full. And there are sesame seeds on the bottom of his cage, but his feeder only has milo, millet, sunflower, and safflower. My cousin has a parrot and uses the same feed."

Veronica was **agog**. She'd been betrayed by her own bird. She thanked me and asked what she owed me. I told her I couldn't accept her money and that I should be going.

"I haven't had breakfast yet," I said. "And solving mysteries makes me hungry."

"Then stay and eat here," Veronica said. "I'm making breakfast burgers."

---

agog interested and excited; eager

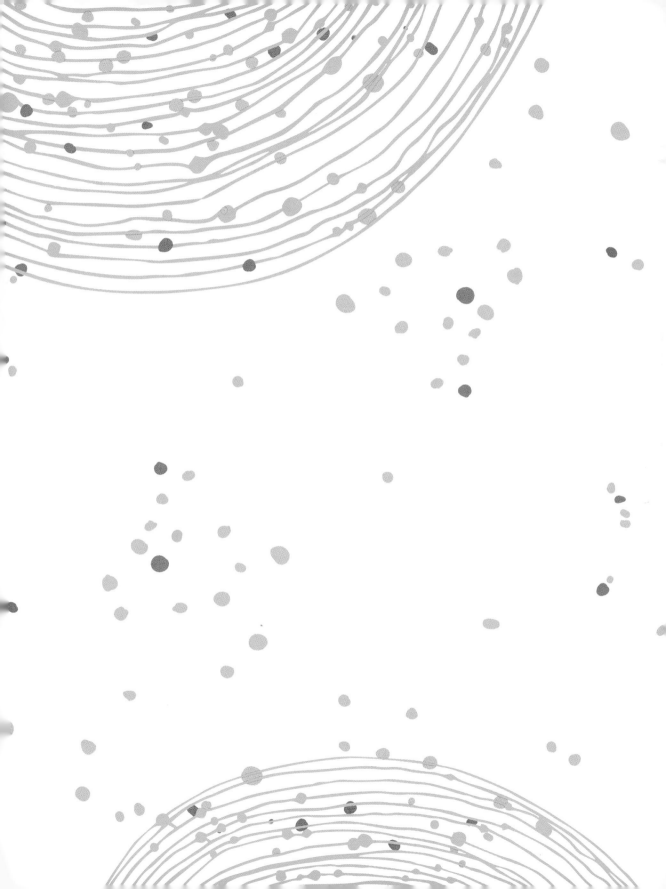

The Mystery of the Topaz Heart

Edgerton was a small town. Actually, it was a *very* small town. Fewer than five hundred people lived there. It had one park, one restaurant, and one traffic light. Few visitors came to Edgerton, but those who came did so for just one reason: to see the topaz heart.

The topaz heart was, as its name suggests, a heart-shaped topaz. The gem was a beautiful greenish-yellow and as big as a catcher's mitt. It weighed 28 pounds. Indeed, according to experts, it was the largest cut topaz in the world.

The topaz heart was discovered a century ago by Arthur Bell, a local hero in Edgerton. The jewel was then displayed in the Bell Gallery on Sheffield Road in town for the next 98 years. Two years ago, though, something happened. The topaz heart was reported stolen.

William Bell, Arthur Bell's grandson, owned the Bell Gallery at the time. One fateful Tuesday, he arrived at work to find the gallery's front window smashed. Inside, the case that had held the topaz heart was open and the jewel itself was gone. He immediately phoned the police.

The theft was huge news in Edgerton. Any news was huge news in Edgerton. The replacement of a street sign qualified for a banner headline in the *Edgerton Gazette*. But this really was a big deal. Newspapers across the country learned of the theft. Reporters flooded into town to speak to William Bell.

But the first reporter to arrive didn't come from out of town. The first was a writer for the *Edgerton Gazette* itself. Her name was Paula Cortez.

Paula had been born in Edgerton. She left town to attend college and later spent two decades as an **investigative journalist** in New York City. She married there, but she came home when her own daughter was four. She wanted her child to grow up close to family.

So Paula was the first to cover the story. And the first two people Paula spoke to were William Bell and Molly Foster, chief of the Edgerton Police Department. She met them at the Bell Gallery.

"Can you describe what happened?" Paula asked Bell.

Bell, a thin man with blue eyes and a bald head, nodded gravely. He said, "I wake up early, so I was coming up the sidewalk at about 6:30. That's when I saw shattered glass everywhere in front of the gallery."

....

investigative journalist a reporter who investigates, or deeply studies, a topic in preparing a careful news report about it

"From the broken window," Chief Foster added,
pointing to the front of the gallery, where the glass had
yet to be replaced.

"Right," Bell said. "So I hurried in. I rushed to the case,
you know, where the topaz heart was on display. But…"

"It was gone," Chief Foster said, finishing Bell's
thought. "So he called us."

As they walked inside, Paula shook her head
sympathetically. Bell rubbed his head, and Paula
noticed, behind him, a security system keypad on the
wall. It was white with the letters ESS written in blue on
it. Paula pointed at the keypad.

---

sympathetically done with sympathy; with like feeling or understanding

She asked, "Did the alarm go off or had it been disabled?"

"Oh," Bell said, turning to look at the keypad himself, "it was blaring when I arrived. I turned it off after I called 9-1-1."

Paula took some notes. Then she thanked Bell and Foster for speaking with her and stood to leave. Bell said it was a shame that the topaz heart wouldn't be there to attract visitors to Edgerton anymore. Paula agreed.

"I visited this gallery a lot when I was young," she said. "I loved how the light bounced off the topaz. It was beautiful. It's too bad my daughter may not get to see it herself."

Paula walked to the door. Before she left the gallery, though, she stopped. She scratched her chin.

"One more thing," she began. "The topaz heart was insured, right?"

Bell cocked his head to one side. He looked like the thought had never occurred to him. He said, "Of course."

"For a lot of money, I bet. Several million, right?" Paula continued before catching herself. "I'm sorry. I shouldn't have said that. I know the topaz heart was a family **heirloom**."

"That's right," Bell said, smiling gently.

"I didn't mean to suggest anything."

"It's okay."

....

heirloom a thing of special value handed down from one generation to another

Then Paula thanked Bell and Foster again and left the gallery. As she drove down Sheffield Road afterward, she saw four news vans heading in the opposite direction. It looked like William Bell and Molly Foster had several more interviews in their future. It would be a busy afternoon for them and for her.

• • •

The rest of the story hardly needs to be told. Within a week, William Bell was arrested. Chief Foster slapped the cuffs on him herself. His trial was set for the following month.

Paula testified at the trial. She told how she went right to Edgerton Security Services, the alarm company. She described how they told her that the gallery's alarm never went off that Tuesday morning. Then she explained that she listened to Bell's 9-1-1 call. There was no alarm sounding in the background.

Next Paula talked about her visit to the insurance company. There she learned that Bell had recently increased the amount the topaz heart was insured for. Its disappearance would make him very rich. Finally, Paula was asked when she knew for sure that Bell was responsible for the incident.

"Immediately," Paula said.

"How?" asked the lawyer.

"The glass from the gallery's front window," Paula explained. "It was on the sidewalk outside. So the window had to have been broken from inside. It had to be Bell."

It took an hour for the jury to convict William Bell.

As for the topaz heart, it was recovered. Bell had hidden it in his bedroom closet. Today, it's again on display. It's back in its protective case in a gallery on Sheffield Road, where it is once again pretty much the only reason anyone visits Edgerton.

The gallery used to be called the Bell Gallery. Not anymore. Now it's called the Cortez Gallery.

Frontiers of Flight

Go, John Glenn!

by Brian Floca

This was not the part that made a person want to be an astronaut.

While Mission Control checked the weather and double-checked the rocket, John Glenn waited. He was strapped in a cramped space capsule, *Friendship 7*. For almost four hours he waited, on his back, his feet pushed up in front of him.

He thought of astronaut Alan Shepard, strapped into his capsule, waiting for launch a year earlier. "Why don't you fix your little problem … and light this candle?" Shepard had asked Mission Control. Glenn smiled at the memory. He quietly reviewed his checklist, and waited.

Finally the countdown moved toward zero. Below Glenn's back, the nine stories of fuel and rocket began to stir. "You have firing signal," Mission Control announced. "Godspeed, John Glenn."

Flames flickered and then rolled in great red clouds from the base of the rocket. Then, with Glenn perched on its peak, it tore free of the Earth.

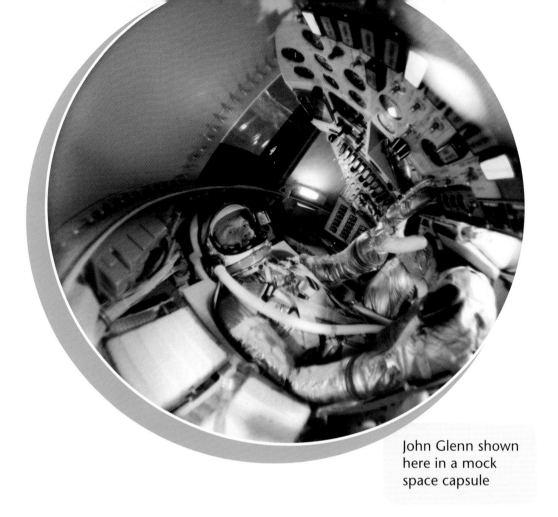

John Glenn shown here in a mock space capsule

As John Glenn rode into the sky on February 20, 1962, America held its breath. The United States was in second place in the "Space Race" that had begun in 1957, when the Soviet Union launched *Sputnik,* the first **artificial satellite**. Now John Glenn's attempt to be the first American in orbit gave Americans new hope of catching up.

....

artificial satellite a manufactured body that orbits another larger body, such as a weather satellite; a familiar natural satellite is the moon, which orbits the earth

Across the country, people gathered around televisions and radios. In New York City, subway loudspeakers came to life in a burst of static. "Attention, ladies and gentlemen," they announced. "Colonel John H. Glenn has just taken off in his rocket for orbit. Please say a little prayer for him."

"It's a little bumpy along here," Glenn radioed. Then the rocket, its fuel used up, detached and tumbled toward Earth.

Now the *Friendship 7* capsule was speeding smoothly in orbit. "Capsule is turning around," Glenn reported. And then, "Oh, that view is tremendous!"

Below rolled the wide, blue Earth. Rivers and continents spread out like pages in an atlas. Lightning flickered through storms on the Atlantic. Moonlight silvered the clouds over Africa. On darkened Australia, city lights glowed brightly, turned on as a beacon for the astronaut far overhead.

Over the Pacific, water droplets from the capsule froze into ice particles. They caught the sunlight and floated around *Friendship 7*, looking like fireflies dancing in space.

With each hour-and-a-half orbit of Earth, Glenn watched the sun rise and set. He smiled as he radioed Mission Control, "That was about the shortest day I have ever run into."

But Mission Control seemed distracted. A warning light had captured the flight team's attention. The warning light said a heat shield was loose.

This shield was attached to the capsule's base. It was there to protect the ship on its way back to Earth. When *Friendship 7* reentered Earth's atmosphere, friction against the air would build up a blazing temperature of 4,000°F around the ship. Only the heat shield would allow the capsule and Glenn to survive.

On his third orbit, Glenn received unexpected instructions from Mission Control: "We are recommending you leave the **retro-package** on through entire reentry." The retro-package was made up of small rockets strapped over the heat shield. They were designed to slow the capsule on its return to Earth. Glenn had been trained to release the retro-pack after firing it. So now he knew something was wrong.

"This is *Friendship 7*," he radioed. "What is the reason for this? Do you have any reason? Over."

"Not at this time," replied Mission Control. But Glenn began to put together the pieces. Perhaps, if the heat shield was loose, the retro-package could hold the shield in place long enough for the capsule to survive. All Glenn could do was hope it would work.

....

retro-package a system of retro-rockets, backup or supplementary engines, on a spacecraft, used in slowing down

After three orbits, the capsule turned around, putting its blunt end forward. The retro-pack fired, and *Friendship 7* began the long fall back to Earth.

For twenty minutes, the capsule bucked and lunged while the temperature around it climbed. As Glenn watched the sky about him turn a brilliant orange, flaming chunks of the spacecraft streaked past his small window. "And at that time," he later remembered, "I couldn't be absolutely certain whether it was the retro-pack or the heat shield tearing off…. It didn't do any good to panic at that point."

The hot gases surrounding the capsule blocked all communication. The flight team at Mission Control could only lean forward, listen, and hope.

Finally, Glenn's voice burst through the long silence. "Boy, that was a real fireball!" Five hours and 81,000 miles after he had taken off, John Glenn splashed down to a welcome grander than any since Charles Lindbergh had crossed the Atlantic.

Four million people braved the March cold to attend the astronaut's ticker-tape parade in New York City. Grown men, even New York City police officers, wept just to see John Glenn go by.

John Glenn's homecoming parade in Cambridge, Ohio, celebrates his successful mission to orbit Earth in 1962.

Today, there are no ticker-tape parades when the space shuttle returns from one of its many missions. But that only shows how far space flight has come since John Glenn's flight in *Friendship 7*, when space was all race and risk.

Project Mercury's 50th Anniversary

Interview with John Glenn

Interview by Audie Cornish

February 20, 2012

GLENN: Well, a liftoff is very, very gentle, contrary to what most people think. Because you remember, the weight of the booster—the amount of thrust on the engine is just barely enough to get the booster underway. And so it's a very gentle liftoff, contrary to what most people think when they see all the fire and smoke of launch. But once you get on up there, then you're burned out—you're burning out your fuel as you go up and you're very light on fuel. Then just insertion into orbit, and that's where the highest strain on the body is, about 7, almost 8 Gs at that time. But the direction of Gs was like you're—if you were lying flat on your bed and had your bed accelerating rapidly up toward the ceiling, that would—that's the direction of the Gs, straight into your chest.

CORNISH: Prior to your trip 50 years ago, there were unmanned U.S. rockets that exploded on the launch pads. Can you remember what you were feeling that day the moment of takeoff for *Friendship 7*?

GLENN: Well, there had been a number of failures but we weren't going out to ride a failure. And we felt they'd corrected all the difficulties with the boosters before that time and the launch problems. And so we had a lot of confidence that there was going to be a successful mission. We weren't off on some suicide effort, certainly. So we thought that the odds of things working OK were up in the upper 90 percent or we wouldn't have gone. But the— there were some problems cropped up on the flight but was able to take care of those OK and—although they were things that we hadn't really trained that much for. But it was the time of the Cold War and so there were was a lot of pressure on the—to get going and the Russians were claiming that they were—Soviets were claiming they were ahead of us in technology. And so it was against that backdrop that the early space flights took off.

John Glenn speaks in Cleveland, Ohio, on February 20, 2012, the fiftieth anniversary of his historic flight aboard *Friendship 7.*

John Glenn and Friendship 7

from Profile of John Glenn NASA.gov

John Glenn will always be remembered as the first American to orbit Earth. Glenn's flight on *Friendship 7* was a national triumph, but problems arose that could have spelled **disaster**. The first was a failure of the **automatic** control system.

During the first orbit, Glenn was to test to see if the **capsule** could be flown **manually**. When the automatic system went out at the end of the first orbit, it became a matter of life and death.

"I went to manual control and continued in that **mode** during the second and third orbits, and during reentry," Glenn recalled later. He had been **confident** he could do it.

....

disaster a sudden destructive event

automatic acting or done with no thought or decision; done mechanically by machine without need for human guidance

capsule a small vehicle or closed compartment for travel in space

manually done by hand and not by machine

mode form, way, or manner of doing something

confident certain, sure, or positive; having or showing sureness or certainty

John Glenn enters the *Friendship 7* capsule, February 20, 1962.

"The **malfunction** just forced me to prove very rapidly what had been planned over a longer period of time."

Another problem seemed even more serious. The instruments showed the spacecraft's heat shield was loose. It seemed possible that Glenn and the spacecraft would burn up on reentry. Much of the world held its breath.

Glenn left the retro-rocket pack in place to steady the heat shield during reentry. "It made for a very **spectacular** reentry from where I was sitting," he said. Big chunks of the burning material came flying by the window.

He wasn't sure whether the flaming debris was the rocket pack or the heat shield breaking up. "Fortunately," he told an interviewer, "it was the rocket pack, or I wouldn't be answering these questions."

....

malfunction failure to function, or work, properly
spectacular showy, dramatic, or sensational

Two Views of Project Mercury

I was seven when my dad started working for NASA. I know now that he was a **thermodynamic engineer** on Project Mercury. Back then, I just knew he was a scientist.

Dad always had on a white shirt and a tie when he left for work. His glasses had metal frames. He wore his salt-and-pepper hair in a crew cut. When he kissed me goodbye, he smelled like coffee and aftershave.

I couldn't tell you what he looked like when he came home, though. I was never awake for that. Dad—like everyone at NASA—worked long hours in those days. Some nights I'd hear him and Mom chatting downstairs after midnight. But I never once heard him complain about work.

I missed him, of course. Mom and I ate a lot of dinners without him in those years. He missed a few of my ballet recitals. But I never got angry about that. I knew he

....

thermodynamic engineer a technical professional who applies the theories of heat and energy transfer to solve technical or mechanical problems

would have liked to be with us, and I knew Dad's job was important. He was going to help put John Glenn into space and make sure he came back home safely.

I asked him about the mission when I was 11. I wanted to know whether he thought it would succeed. I remember he smiled, took off his glasses, and spoke in a very calm voice.

"It's **complicated**, Donna," Dad said. "But I work with the smartest people in the world. Together, we'll figure out how to get Lieutenant Colonel Glenn up and down. I know we will."

Dad's confidence comforted me. He was so sure that science could make the impossible possible. He was certain that he and his coworkers could overcome any obstacle.

February 20, 1962, was a Tuesday and I had a fever. Mom made me toast with raspberry jelly on it, and we watched the launch of *Friendship 7* on TV. It was a little before ten in the morning, and I was lying on the couch.

I never saw so much smoke in my life! As the rocket lifted off the launching pad, I wondered how John Glenn felt in that tiny capsule on top of it. I wondered how Dad felt watching the rocket shoot into the sky. I wondered how all of his coworkers felt. I looked over, and I saw Mom wipe a tear from her eye. I knew how she felt: proud.

....

complicated hard to understand or explain

I fell asleep after that. My fever was going up, I guess. I dreamed that my dad and I were walking in a park, and he was carrying a whole **skyscraper** on his shoulders. When I asked how he was doing that, he just smiled and said, "Hard work."

I woke up in time to hear that *Friendship 7* had just splashed down safely. John Glenn was in good condition, waiting to be picked up by a Navy ship. I was happy, but not surprised that the mission was a success.

After all, my dad was one of the smartest people in the world.

· · ●

John Glenn sat in his capsule, *Friendship 7*. It was the morning of February 20, 1962. He was about to become the first American to orbit Earth. But the launch was delayed.

Glenn was **frustrated**, but he understood the situation. He was an experienced pilot. He was also an American hero. He'd served in World War II and the Korean War. NASA would not risk his life or the success of the mission, Project Mercury, by launching *Friendship 7* a moment too soon.

----

skyscraper a very tall building
frustrated feeling discouraged or prevented from meeting a goal

Plus, in the grand scheme of things, the delay was minor. It was a hiccup. The launch could wait a few hours. After all, that morning was years in the making.

Project Mercury began in 1958 with three goals. It aimed to put a manned spacecraft into orbit. It aimed to test how humans functioned in space. And it aimed to return the craft and its pilot safely to Earth.

Naturally, the public was most interested in the Project Mercury pilots. They were going to be the first astronauts. They were the faces of the mission. They were its **celebrities**.

But there were dozens of milestones that had to be passed before the pilots could shoot toward the stars. And the pilots were far from the mission's only important players. Just as critical to Project Mercury's success was a group of people whose names never made the headlines.

This group was made up of thousands of scientists and engineers. The public rarely heard from them. Their pictures seldom appeared in newspapers. Yet they were the mission's unsung heroes.

These scientists and engineers designed, built, and tested rockets. They launched unmanned capsules and returned them safely to Earth. They studied the effects of zero-gravity and developed methods to deal with it.

....

celebrities famous, or *celebrated*, people

Some worked with only the most basic computer technology. Others worked without any computers whatsoever. All worked incredibly long hours. They dealt with countless setbacks and failures.

With each milestone came new challenges. With each solution came new problems. Yet the unsung heroes met every challenge and solved every problem. They poured their energy, their determination, and their intelligence into the mission.

So as John Glenn waited in *Friendship 7*, they were ready to see their hard work pay off.

Friendship 7 did eventually lift off that morning. As it rose skyward, it carried just one person. But it also carried the dedication and skill of thousands of America's best and brightest minds. It carried the innovations they developed and the sacrifices they made. *Friendship 7*'s launch, and Project Mercury's ultimate success, was a testament to the talents of those unsung heroes.

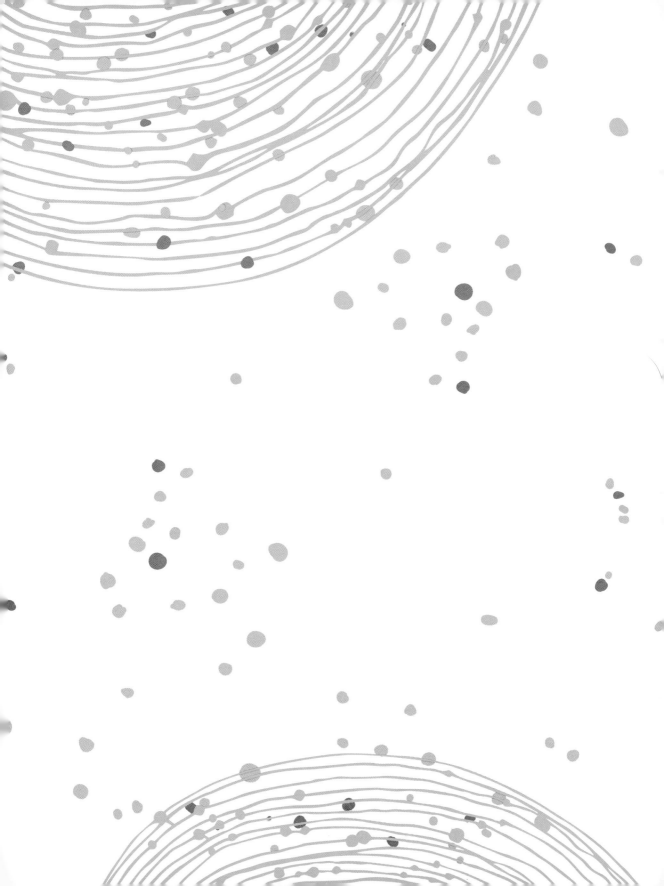

Wilbur and Orville Wright
Men with Wings

Wilbur

Orville

by Dorothy Haas

"Which of the Wright brothers," people sometimes ask, "was more responsible for inventing the airplane?"

The brothers would have laughed at such a question. For the answer is: one was as responsible as the other! They thought as a team; when one had an idea, the other was sure to improve on it. And they worked as a team; when they flew their gliders and, finally, their plane, each took a turn at the controls while the other acted as assistant. The airplane is the amazing result of true teamwork.

● ● ●

"Katharine?"

A pretty, dark-haired woman hurried into the front hall of a big old home in Dayton, Ohio. She looked up the stairway. Her father, Bishop Milton Wright, was leaning out of his study door.

"Was there any mail from the boys?" he asked.

Katharine Wright shook her head. "Not a word," she said. "Certainly they must have tested their plane by now! And—" she sighed, "oh, Father, I hope they'll be home for Christmas! Why—why, it's only a week away! And Christmas just wouldn't be Christmas without Wilbur and Orville here at home...."

"Careful—watch that wing!"

"Some wind! Must be blowin' up to twenty-five miles an hour! Fasten those ropes!"

Seven men crowded around a machine, a flying machine, on a lonely strip of beach at Kitty Hawk, North Carolina. They were trying to keep the machine from being carried away by a wind that whipped the sand into clouds around them.

Five of the men wore seamen's clothing. They were from the Life Saving Station on Kill Devil Hill at Kitty Hawk. The other two men wore business suits and high starched collars.

"Set it down on the track," said Wilbur Wright. "But hang on until we get the guide ropes tightened."

"Too bad you have to make your tests today in this wind," said one of the seamen.

"Tomorrow might be just as windy," answered Orville Wright. "And besides, we couldn't wait many more days and still hope to be home for Christmas."

They fastened the ropes to the airplane and stood back. The wind quieted for a minute. In the silence could be heard the dull roar of the mighty Atlantic. The lonely cries of sea gulls echoed overhead.

"My stomach says it's nearly noon," said one of the seamen.

Wilbur took out his big silver watch. "So it is," he said, looking at it. "Well, let's try just once more before we stop to have something to eat."

"It's your turn to fly the machine, Will," said Orville. "Remember to use a light hand on that rudder."

It was December 17, 1903. Wilbur and Orville Wright had already made three very short flights that morning. They had flown as far as 175 feet, and had been airborne about twenty seconds on the longest of these flights.

These had been unsteady, up-and-down flights. The plane would rise to fourteen feet from the ground, and then it would dart, suddenly, to within ten feet. The brothers hoped to make a longer flight. They wanted to prove beyond doubt that this was a real, motor-driven flight, and not just a wind-lifted glide.

Many men in the past had thought of flying. Some had even tried. They had been able to fly gliders for very short distances. But nobody had been able to put a motor-powered plane in the air and keep it there.

Wilbur and Orville Wright believed this could be done. They did not listen to people who laughed and said, "If men had been meant to fly, they would have been given wings."

As boys they flew kites. They tried to understand what kept the kites in the air. And they watched the birds. "See how the birds use their wings," they said. "They certainly know things about the air that we don't know!"

When they grew up they built a glider. They flew that. They made many hundreds of glider flights. Then they decided to build an airplane that would stay in the air longer than a glider could.

Their ideas were different from those anybody else had. And so they built a small wind tunnel and tested these new ideas. And at last, in their little bicycle shop in Dayton, they built their plane.

It was made of light wood, wire, and canvas. Even using these light materials, they figured it would weigh nearly 750 pounds with a man in it.

It was powered by a **four-cylinder gasoline engine** that could deliver twelve **horsepower**. Instead of wheels, the plane had runners like a sled. These runners rested on a track about sixty feet long. The plane moved along this track until it picked up enough speed to take off.

After they had their plane built, they decided to take it to Kitty Hawk to test it. "The winds there are usually steady at this time of year," they said. "And besides—the sand is soft, if we should have an accident!"

four-cylinder gasoline engine a gas engine with four piston chambers (cylinders)

horsepower unit of power equal to the work done in lifting 550 pounds one foot per second

After months of hard work, they were going to find out if their ideas were good. They were going to find out if their plane would really fly.

A brisk gust of wind caught at Wilbur's cap. He reached up and turned his cap around so that it wouldn't blow off his head. Then he turned up his coat collar and climbed into the plane. He lay down on his stomach and grasped the steering wires.

"Start the motor, Orv," he called back over his shoulder.

Orville worked over the little motor for a minute. It coughed. Then it caught hold. The plane shuddered.

"All right, men," Orville called. As the rope holding the plane slipped away, it moved slowly down the track. Then it picked up speed. Orville ran beside it, steadying the wings.

He didn't need to run the full length of the track. As the plane picked up speed it rose into the air.

"Good luck, Will," Orville shouted over the roar of the motor. He stopped running and watched the plane lift uncertainly into the air. Once again it flew unsteadily for a short distance. Then, caught by the wind, it dipped dangerously near the earth.

"Ahh-hh-hh ..." chorused the men who watched.

"Lift that left wing, Will!" Orville shouted, unmindful that his brother could not hear him.

Then, as suddenly as it had dipped, the plane righted itself. Orville held his breath. Would it be able to ...? It

Wilbur Wright watches brother Orville take off in their Wright Flyer at Kitty Hawk, North Carolina, December 17, 1903.

would—and did! The plane leveled off and flew an even, steady, controlled course!

"Just look at it go!" shouted one of the men.

"He's really flyin'!" cried another.

Orville let out his breath. He stood looking after the plane. Flight! Motor-powered flight! For the first time in history, man was actually flying!

Suddenly one of the plane's wings tilted. A fresh gust of wind caught it. The plane pitched toward the earth. It came to rest on a small, sandy dune. The motor died. The screams of the sea gulls were loud in the stillness.

The men ran forward. Their feet slipped in the shifting sand. As they drew near they saw Wilbur scrambling out of the plane.

"Will! Will!" Orville called. "Are you all right?"

Will grinned at them as they puffed across the dune and crowded around him. "I'm just fine," he said. "And, Orv, we did it! I just checked the watch. I was up fifty-nine seconds, and"—he looked back at the starting track—"covered something more than eight hundred feet!"

The seamen pumped the brothers' hands. "Congratulations!" they shouted.

"Most amazing thing I ever saw!" said one of them in wonder. He glanced up at the sea gulls soaring overhead. "Not quite as spry as them gulls up there," he laughed. "But I wouldn't doubt," he said, looking from one brother to the other, "that soon you men will be outflyin' them birds!"

Bishop Wright looked up from the slip of yellow paper that had just been delivered to him. He was smiling. "It's from Orville," he said. "They flew their airplane. It says here that they made four flights in it!"

Katharine clasped her hands. "Oh, Father," she said. "How very happy they must be! I'm proud of them!"

"And," Bishop Wright went on, "you'll be pleased about this, my dear, he says they'll be—"

Katharine's eyes sparkled. She didn't give her father time to finish the sentence. She flew to the dining-room door. "Carrie!" she called. "Will you order an extra-big turkey, please? Mr. Orville and Mr. Wilbur will be"—she turned and flashed a smile at her father—"*home for Christmas*!"

The Challenge
Bessie Coleman's Story

by Margaret Roberts

The little airplane soared higher and higher into the clear blue sky. Every face in the crowd was turned upward, watching. The only sound was the plane's engine. It grew fainter as the plane went higher.

Suddenly the plane flipped upside down. It began to fall, almost like a leaf, turning over and over. The silence on the ground exploded into a great cry. But the cry turned to laughter as the plane righted itself and began to climb again.

In a flash the pilot leveled the aircraft and began a series of snap rolls. The plane spun like a top. The crowd yelled and cheered.

The show of **aerial acrobatics** ended ten minutes later as the plane came in for a perfect landing. The pilot, thirty-year-old Bessie Coleman, hopped down from

....

aerial acrobatics trick, or stunt, flying

the open cockpit. She grinned as she took off her goggles and unbuttoned her heavy jacket.

The date was September 3, 1922. Orville and Wilbur Wright had flown the first airplane less than twenty years ago. Now, who was this incredible woman?

Bessie Coleman, the first black woman to fly an airplane, was born January 26, 1892. She was the tenth of thirteen children. When Bessie was nine years old, her father left the family home in Texas and never returned. To earn money for food and clothing, the children picked cotton on a nearby plantation. Their mother took in washing and did maid work for a white family in town.

Bessie was a good student. She completed all eight grades at the school for black children. She wanted to continue her education. But in those days white people and black people went to separate schools. Unfortunately, there was no black high school close enough for Bessie to attend.

As a young teenager, Bessie dreamed of becoming a famous pilot. It seemed an impossible goal. But Bessie was never one to shy away from challenges. She had great determination and confidence. Carefully, she made a plan.

First, she had to earn money for flying lessons. She began by taking in washing. She walked four miles into town to pick up the laundry. She carried it home. She scrubbed the garments, starched them, wrung them out by hand, and hung them on a clothesline to dry. Then she pressed the clothes with a heavy iron heated on the kitchen stove.

It was hard, unpleasant, boring work. But Bessie never felt humbled by it. She was willing to work at anything that would bring her closer to her goal.

By day she worked. At night she read the books she constantly borrowed from the town library.

By the time she was nineteen, Bessie had earned enough money to take her next step. She moved to Chicago. There she took classes in a beauty school for African Americans. Through the months of training, she walked the cold winter streets to classes. Her savings lasted just long enough for her to complete the course.

For the next five years, Bessie worked in the White Sox Barber Shop. She manicured the nails of customers while they had their shaves and haircuts. She took a second job working at a chili parlor. She saved her money. When she had enough, she began to look for a flying school.

She quickly learned that all doors to **aviation** were closed to her. A black woman wanting to fly airplanes? Unthinkable! But Bessie Coleman refused to take no for an answer.

She introduced herself to Robert S. Abbott. He was the African American owner of the *Chicago Defender*, a respected newspaper in the city. She hoped he would have some ideas for her, and he did.

A few women were flying in France, he said. He suggested she learn to speak some French, and then go to France to become a pilot.

Bessie studied French until her teacher thought she could "get by." Then, with help from Mr. Abbott and some of his friends, she traveled on a ship to France. Bessie was grateful to Mr. Abbott. She once told a newspaper reporter, "He is the man who gave me my chance. I will never forget him."

In France, the first flight school Bessie visited refused to accept her. They said that two women students had recently been killed in crashes. That did not scare Bessie. She found another school. At last, she began to learn to fly.

Shortly after she began her flight training, Bessie saw an accident. One of the male student pilots was killed.

....

aviation the aircraft industry; the development, design, manufacture, and operation—flying—of planes

Bessie Coleman, American aviator, c. 1920

"It was a terrible shock to my nerves," she wrote, "but I never lost them. I kept going."

After ten months of tough training, Bessie passed all the tests. She stayed an extra month to learn aerial acrobatics. In September 1921 she sailed back to the United States—the world's first licensed black woman pilot.

Bessie had kept in touch with Robert Abbott. In New York, he proudly arranged her first American show. The announcement stated:

*Chicago **Aviatrix** to show New Yorkers how she does her stuff! Bessie Coleman will give an aerial acrobatic exhibition on August 27th. This will be her first flight in America!*

Rain canceled the show. But a few days later Bessie performed at Glenn Curtiss Field in Long Island, New York. Soon after, she put on a show at Checkerboard Field in Chicago. Bessie gave a dazzling performance. She did loop-the-loops, slow rolls, snap rolls, and tailspins. The crowd went wild.

After that, Bessie became a celebrity. She performed acrobatic flights all over the country, sometimes alone and sometimes with small groups of pilots who had flown in World War I.

Early in 1924, Bessie had an accident. Her plane's engine failed. Several broken ribs, a broken leg, and many cuts and bruises could not stop her. In the hospital, she told a reporter, "You just tell the world that I'm coming back!" And, of course, she did.

In 1925, as she toured the country, Bessie began giving lectures in schools, churches, and theaters. She urged African American audiences to get involved in aviation. There would soon be great opportunities, she said, and

aviatrix a woman aviator, that is, a pilot

they must be a part of them. Partly because of Bessie Coleman, many young African American men became military pilots during World War II.

On April 29, 1926, disaster struck again. Bessie and another pilot were in the air. But someone had carelessly left a wrench lying loose in the cockpit. It slipped and jammed the airplane's control stick into the full-forward position. This sent the plane into a dive from which it could not recover. Both pilots were killed. Bessie was just thirty-four years old.

Bessie Coleman has not been forgotten. In 1990, the mayor of Chicago honored her memory by giving the name "Bessie Coleman Drive" to a highway leading to busy O'Hare International Airport. In 1992, the city leaders in Chicago wrote, "Bessie Coleman continues to inspire untold thousands of young persons with her sense of adventure, her positive attitude, and her determination to succeed." In 1995, the U.S. Postal Service issued a stamp in her honor. It shows Bessie in her leather flying helmet and jacket, ready to climb into the cockpit and soar high above the earth.

BLACK HERITAGE

USA
32

BESSIE COLEMAN

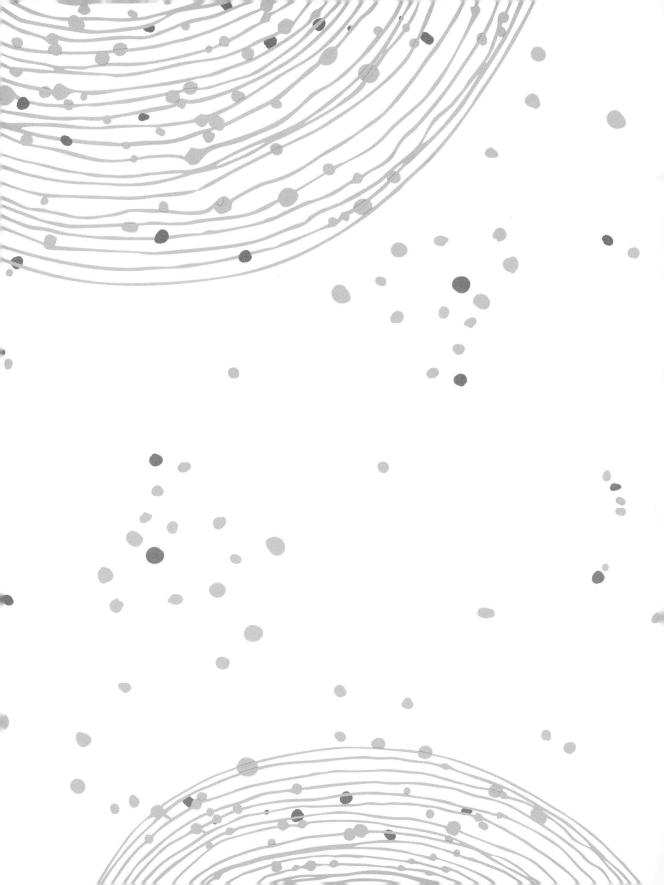

Dangerous Adventure!
Lindbergh's Famous Flight

by Ruth Belov Gross

Charles Lindbergh grew up on a farm in Minnesota. One of the things he loved best was to lie in the tall grass and look up at the sky. Charles wished he had wings. "How wonderful it would be to fly," Charles thought.

When Charles was ten, his mother took him to an air show. Charles had never seen an airplane before. Most people had never seen an airplane. Airplanes were something new.

The first airplanes couldn't fly very fast. They couldn't go very far or very high. And they were only big enough for one or two people. The propeller was in back. The pilot sat outside, in the front.

Mrs. Lindbergh told Charles that airplanes were dangerous. She didn't want him to go up in an airplane—ever. Suppose the engine stopped, she said. Suppose a wing fell off. He could be killed!

But Charles kept thinking about flying. He imagined he had wings and could fly through the air—over fences, over the tops of trees, over the roof of his house.

Eleven years later, Charles Lindbergh had his own plane and was really flying. He was 21 years old.

Airplanes were still new and strange to most people. When a plane flew over a house or barn, everyone would run outside to look at it. When a plane landed in a cow field, the farmers would come right up close—and so would the cows.

Pilots earned money by taking people up for rides in their planes. A pilot would stay in one town for a few days, sell as many rides as he could, and then go on to another town. This was called *barnstorming*.

At first, Charles barnstormed with another pilot. Just before they landed in a new town, Charles would walk out on the wing of the plane—while it was still flying! Sometimes he jumped off the wing with a parachute.

The pilot got more customers when Charles did tricks like this. Soon the newspapers were writing about Charles. They called him Daredevil Lindbergh. His friends, though, called him Slim.

Later, Slim barnstormed by himself. He did all kinds of tricks with his plane—spins and loops and rolls.

Barnstorming was a good way to earn money in the summer. But nobody wanted to pay for a plane ride when it was cold and snowy.

Lindbergh needed a job he could do all year round. When he was 24 years old, he got a job flying bags of mail from one city to another. It was easy to fly the mail in the daytime. At night, though, flying could be dangerous. Pilots couldn't always see where they were going—or where they were landing.

On two different nights, Lindbergh had to jump out of his plane with a parachute. Once he landed in a cornfield. Once he landed on top of a barbed wire fence.

Both times, the planes were wrecked. But the bags of mail were still in good shape. Lindbergh got the mail out of the wreckage and sent it on by train.

One night in September 1926, Lindbergh was flying the mail from St. Louis, Missouri, to Chicago, Illinois. It was a beautiful clear night. Lindbergh wished he could keep on flying and never stop.

What would he need to keep on flying for a really long time? The plane he was flying now couldn't go more than three or four hours without running out of gas.

He'd need a plane with gas tanks that could hold a lot of gas. And he'd need a much better engine—an engine that could keep going for hours and hours. If he had the right kind of plane, he could fly all night—or longer.

He could even fly from New York City to Paris, France!

Paris was on the other side of the Atlantic Ocean— about 3600 miles from New York. When Lindbergh carried the mail, he only had to fly 285 miles.

Lindbergh had heard about a prize, $25,000, for the first person who could fly between New York and Paris without stopping. He could be that person. Why not?

He would fly alone. It might take him from one morning to the next night. But he could stay awake that long.

By the time Lindbergh landed in Chicago, he had made up his mind. He would try for the prize.

First he had to get a plane. Lindbergh had $2000 saved up, but he couldn't buy a plane for $2000.

Charles Lindbergh was first to fly solo nonstop across the Atlantic Ocean.

He was living in St. Louis then. Some businessmen in St. Louis knew what a good pilot Lindbergh was. The men wanted him to be the first pilot to fly nonstop from New York to Paris. So they got together and said they would give Lindbergh the rest of the money for the plane.

Lindbergh knew just what kind of plane he wanted—a monoplane with one engine. But the people who made airplanes would not sell him that kind of plane. They did not think he could get to Paris alive.

"What?" they said. "You want to fly alone? In a plane with only one engine?"

The plane would crash, they said. Then everybody would think their planes were no good.

Charles Lindbergh had to find a plane soon. It was wintertime now, and he knew that some pilots were making plans to fly to Paris in the spring. He wanted to get there before they did.

The others already had their planes—big, heavy planes that could hold as many as four people.

At the end of February, Lindbergh took the train to California. He was hoping that a small company would agree to make a plane for him. And they did. They said they would make exactly the kind of plane Lindbergh wanted.

Every single day for two months, Lindbergh and the plane people worked on the plane. Sometimes they worked all night. By the end of April, the plane was finished. It was a shiny silver plane, the most beautiful plane Lindbergh had ever seen.

Charles Lindbergh and *Spirit of St. Louis*

Lindbergh gave his plane a name—*Spirit of St. Louis.* That was his way of thanking the men in St. Louis who had paid for the plane.

Now Lindbergh really had to hurry. At least three other planes were almost ready to fly across the Atlantic. What if one of those planes started out before he could even get to New York?

Lindbergh left California on May 10, 1927. First, he flew the *Spirit of St. Louis* to St. Louis. He made the overnight trip in 14 hours and 25 minutes—and set a record.

The next morning, May 12, he took off from St. Louis. He landed in New York, at Curtiss Field, 7 hours and 20 minutes later. Another record!

Newspaper reporters and photographers were waiting for Lindbergh when he landed. Soon everybody was talking about him.

The newspapers called him the Flying Fool. He hated the name. And he didn't like the crowds that followed him wherever he went. He wished he could be alone in his plane, flying over the Atlantic Ocean. But there was more work to be done on the plane. And the weather was bad—rain in New York and storms over the ocean.

By May 19, Lindbergh had been at the airfield for a week. He was fed up.

Lindbergh's friends tried to make him feel better. "Let's go to a play," one of them said. But they never got to the play. On the way, they called the Weather Bureau. Good news! There was a sudden change in the weather. Maybe Lindbergh could leave in the morning!

Lindbergh rushed back to the airfield. He knew that two other planes would be getting ready to take off for Paris. But the airfield was quiet. What were the other pilots waiting for? Good weather all the way to Paris?

Lindbergh wasn't going to wait. He would start for Paris in the morning. As an airmail pilot, he had learned to start out—and then turn back if he had to.

He got to bed around midnight. He couldn't sleep. At 3 o'clock in the morning, Lindbergh was at the airfield again. It was still raining.

He knew he couldn't take off from Curtiss Field. He would need a longer runway when the plane was carrying a full load of gasoline. So, in rainy darkness, a truck dragged the *Spirit of St. Louis* to Roosevelt Field, about a mile away.

Two men poured gas into the tanks, five gallons at a time. At last the tanks held 450 gallons—almost a ton and a half of gas.

The pilots and crews of the other planes were there to say good-bye. No one knew if they would ever see Charles Lindbergh again.

It was after 7 o'clock in the morning when Lindbergh climbed into the cockpit. The runway was muddy. Could he go fast enough in the mud to take off? Was the plane too heavy? Lindbergh had never taken it up with a full load of gas.

He started the engine. What was the matter with the engine? It was turning over too slowly. Maybe the weather was slowing it down. Maybe he shouldn't try to take off today. He had to decide now.

He buckled the safety belt and pulled his goggles over his eyes. He nodded to two men near the plane.

"Let's try it," he said.

The two men pulled the blocks out from under the wheels, and the *Spirit of St. Louis* moved slowly down the muddy runway. Halfway down the runway, the plane made a little hop into the air. It was not moving fast enough to fly. A moment later it bounced back to the ground.

Another hop. Then another. The plane was going faster. Lindbergh was near the end of the runway now. One last try! This time the plane climbed a few feet into the air.

Lindbergh barely missed a tractor standing just beyond the runway. The plane climbed higher. Now Lindbergh was above the telephone wires.

Lindbergh waves from the cockpit of his plane before takeoff.

He was on his way to Paris!

For the next day and a half, Lindbergh would be sitting right where he was now. He couldn't lie down, and he couldn't stand up.

The cockpit was so small, he could touch both sides with his elbows. His head was less than an inch from the roof.

The whole airplane was not even as long as a bus. It had a window on each side and one on top. It did not have a window in front. When Lindbergh wanted to see what was in front of him, he had to use a homemade periscope. There was no toilet on the plane, but there was a metal can with a lid.

Lindbergh had a bottle of water to drink and five sandwiches to eat on the way—two ham sandwiches, two beef sandwiches, and a hard-boiled-egg sandwich.

"Are you only taking five sandwiches?" a friend had asked.

"I won't need more sandwiches if I get to Paris," Lindbergh answered. "And if I don't get to Paris, I won't need more either."

Besides, Lindbergh could get to Paris if he ran out of food. He knew he'd never get there if he ran out of gas. He wanted to have plenty of gas.

Gas was heavy. Every gallon weighed six pounds. So, everything else on the plane had to be very light.

Lindbergh cut holes in his maps and charts so they would be lighter. He tore empty pages out of his notebook. He wasn't taking any extra clothes to wear in Paris. He did not even take a toothbrush.

He weighed every single thing he took with him. He took a rubber life raft in case he had to land at sea. But he didn't take a parachute, because a parachute weighed 20 pounds.

He had two small pocket flashlights instead of regular lights in the cockpit. Lindbergh did not even have a radio. How could he be sure he was heading the right way? He had a compass. And before he left, he figured out his course and marked it on a chart. He would find Paris by following the chart.

By lunchtime, Lindbergh began getting tired and sleepy. The sun was shining into the cockpit and he felt hot. His legs were stiff.

He had a drink of water, but he didn't feel like eating anything. He just wanted to go to sleep.

There were dark clouds ahead—storm clouds. "Stay awake!" he said to himself. "Stay awake!"

The clouds grew bigger and darker. Rain poured down. Lightning flashed. Lindbergh bumped up, down, and sideways in the cockpit. He was sorry he didn't have a parachute.

Soon the storm was over, but not for long. There were more clouds ahead. Lindbergh flew above the clouds, below the clouds, and between the clouds. Sometimes he had to fly right through the clouds. And sometimes he had to fly through fog, blinding white fog.

He got sleepier and more tired. He stamped his feet. He sang a song out loud—very loud.

Lindbergh had been flying for 13 hours. It was dark now. The plane was shaking and bumping again. And the air was cold. Lindbergh zipped up his flying suit and put on his leather mittens and wool-lined helmet. He pulled his flashlight from his pocket and let the light shine on the wings. Ice!

Ice on the wings! He could crash in this icy storm! He thought of turning back. Lindbergh's eyes kept closing. He had to hold them open with his fingers. He had been flying for 27 hours now.

Suddenly he saw a speck on the water. It was a boat! No, it was more than one boat. Those specks were fishing boats. Fishing boats couldn't be far from land. Was he near Ireland?

Lindbergh was wide-awake now. He flew lower, close to the boats. A man stuck his head out of a porthole and looked up at him.

"Which way is Ireland?" Lindbergh yelled.

The man didn't move. Lindbergh thought that the man was too surprised or too scared to answer.

Lindbergh flew on. In less than an hour he was over the rocky tip of Ireland. He saw green fields, roads, wagons, a little village. People ran into the streets and waved up at him.

In the late afternoon, Lindbergh flew over the coast of England. He came to France just as it was getting dark. He had not eaten for almost two days. Now he ate one sandwich and drank some water.

Lindbergh flies *Spirit of St. Louis* over Paris, 1927.

And then he was flying over Paris airport. He saw thousands of lights shining below him. They were the lights of automobiles. Thousands of people had come to welcome him and to light his way.

Charles Lindbergh landed in Paris on the night of May 21, 1927. He had been flying alone for 33 1/2 hours. He had flown from New York to Paris without stopping, something no one had ever done before.

Childhood Classics

The Ecchoing Green

by William Blake

The sun does arise,
And make happy the skies.
The merry bells ring
To welcome the Spring.
The sky-lark and thrush,
The birds of the bush,
Sing louder around,
To the bells' cheerful sound.
While our sports shall be seen
On the Ecchoing Green.

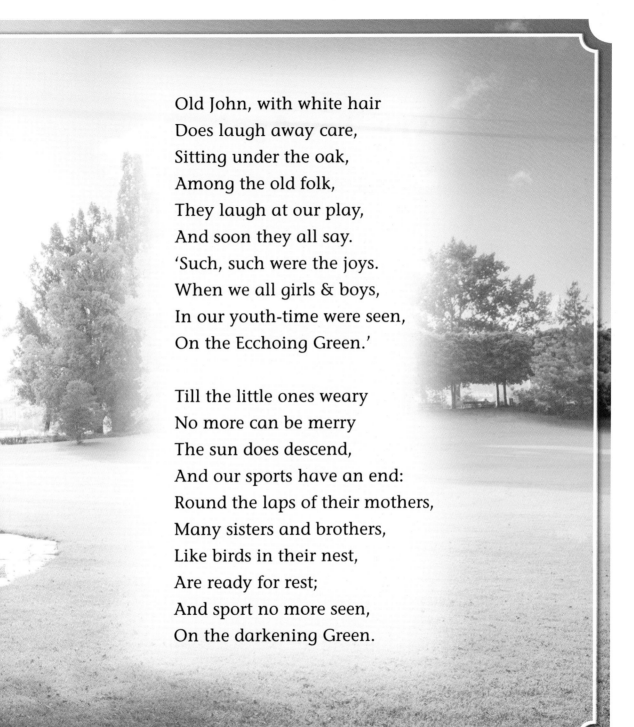

Old John, with white hair
Does laugh away care,
Sitting under the oak,
Among the old folk,
They laugh at our play,
And soon they all say.
'Such, such were the joys.
When we all girls & boys,
In our youth-time were seen,
On the Ecchoing Green.'

Till the little ones weary
No more can be merry
The sun does descend,
And our sports have an end:
Round the laps of their mothers,
Many sisters and brothers,
Like birds in their nest,
Are ready for rest;
And sport no more seen,
On the darkening Green.

Try, Try Again

by T. H. Palmer

'Tis a lesson you should heed,
If at first you don't succeed,
Try, try again;

Then your courage should appear,
For if you will **persevere**,
You will conquer, never fear
Try, try again;

Once or twice, though you should fail,
If you would at last **prevail**,
Try, try again;

persevere to keep trying, keep going, even if it's hard to do
prevail to succeed, achieve, or conquer

If we **strive**, 'tis no **disgrace**
Though we do not win the race;
What should you do in the case?
Try, try again

If you find your task is hard,
Time will bring you your reward,
Try, try again

All that other folks can do,
Why, with patience, should not you?
Only keep this rule in view:
Try, try again.

strive to struggle or try very hard to achieve
something
disgrace a source of shame or dishonor

Bed in Summer

by Robert Louis Stevenson

In winter I get up at night
And dress by yellow candlelight.
In summer, quite the other way,
I have to go to bed by day.

I have to go to bed and see
The birds still hopping on the tree,
Or hear the grown-up people's feet
Still going past me in the street.

And does it not seem hard to you,
When all the sky is clear and blue,
And I should like so much to play,
To have to go to bed by day?

Wynken, Blynken, and Nod

by *Eugene Field*

Wynken, Blynken, and Nod one night
    Sailed off in a wooden shoe,—
Sailed on a river of crystal light
    Into a sea of dew.
"Where are you going, and what do you wish?"
    The old moon asked the three.
"We have come to fish for the herring-fish
    That live in this beautiful sea;
    Nets of silver and gold have we,"
        Said Wynken,
        Blynken,
        And Nod.

The old moon laughed and sang a song,
    As they rocked in the wooden shoe;
And the wind that sped them all night long
    Ruffled the waves of dew;
The little stars were the herring-fish
    That lived in the beautiful sea.
"Now cast your nets wherever you wish,—
    Never afraid are we!"
    So cried the stars to the fishermen three,
        Wynken,
        Blynken,
        And Nod.

All night long their nets they threw
    To the stars in the twinkling foam,—
Then down from the skies came the wooden shoe,
    Bringing the fishermen home:
'Twas all so pretty a sail, it seemed
    As if it could not be;
And some folk thought 'twas a dream they'd dreamed
    Of sailing that beautiful sea;
    But I shall name you the fishermen three:
        Wynken,
        Blynken,
        And Nod.

Wynken and Blynken are two little eyes,
    And Nod is a little head,
And the wooden shoe that sailed the skies
    Is a wee one's trundle-bed;
So shut your eyes while Mother sings
    Of wonderful sights that be,
And you shall see the beautiful things
    As you rock in the misty sea
    Where the old shoe rocked the fishermen three:—
        Wynken,
        Blynken,
        And Nod.

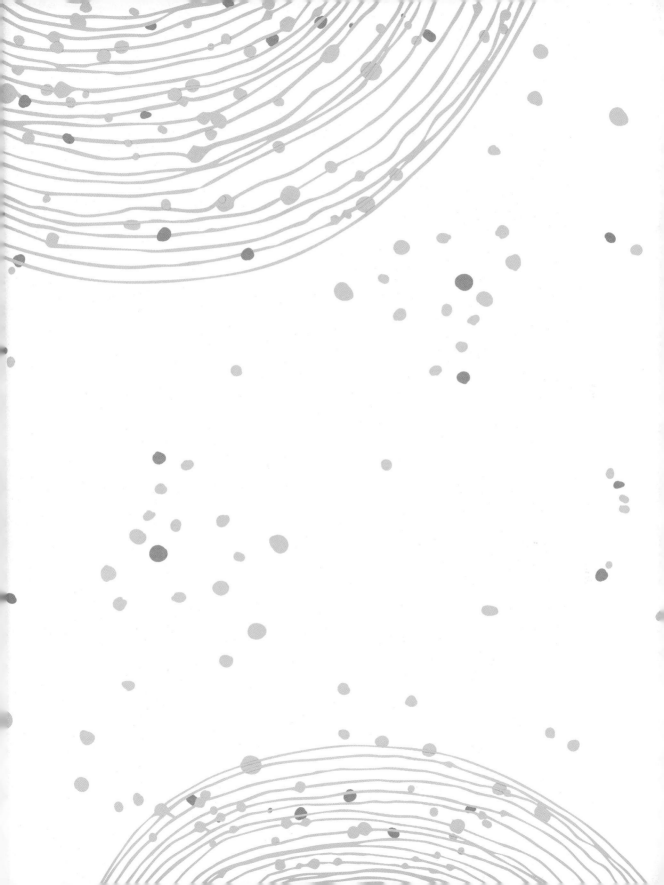

Rikki-Tikki-Tavi

from The Jungle Book *by Rudyard Kipling*

This is the story of the great war that Rikki-tikki-tavi fought single-handed, through the bathrooms of the big bungalow in Segowlee cantonment. Darzee the Tailorbird helped him. And Chuchundra the Muskrat, who never comes out into the middle of the floor, but always creeps round by the wall, gave him advice. But Rikki-tikki did the real fighting.

He was a mongoose, rather like a little cat in his fur and his tail, but quite like a weasel in his head and his habits. His eyes and the end of his restless nose were pink. He could scratch himself anywhere he pleased with any leg, front or back, that he chose to use. He could fluff up his tail till it looked like a bottle brush. And his war cry as he scuttled through the long grass was: *Rikk-tikk-tikki-tikki-tchk!*"

One day, a high summer flood washed him out of the burrow where he lived with his father and mother, and carried him down a roadside ditch. He found a little wisp of grass floating there, and clung to it till he lost his senses. When he revived, he was lying in the hot sun on the middle of a garden path, very draggled indeed, and a small boy was saying, "Here's a dead mongoose. Let's have a funeral."

"No," said his mother," let's take him in and dry him. Perhaps he isn't really dead."

They took him into the house, and a big man picked him up between his finger and thumb and said he was not dead but half choked. So they wrapped him in cotton wool, and warmed him over a little fire, and he opened his eyes and sneezed.

"Now," said the big man (he was an Englishman who had just moved into the bungalow), "don't frighten him, and we'll see what he'll do."

It is the hardest thing in the world to frighten a mongoose, because he is eaten up from nose to tail with curiosity. The motto of all the mongoose family is "Run and find out," and Rikki-tikki was a true mongoose. He looked at the cotton wool, decided that it was not good to eat, ran all round the table, sat up and put his fur in order, scratched himself, and jumped on the small boy's shoulder.

"Don't be frightened, Teddy," said his father. "That's his way of making friends."

"Ouch! He's tickling under my chin," said Teddy.

Rikki-tikki looked down between the boy's collar and neck, snuffed at his ear, and climbed down to the floor, where he sat rubbing his nose.

"Good gracious!" said Teddy's mother, "I suppose he's so tame because we've been kind to him."

"All mongooses are like that," said her husband. "If Teddy doesn't pick him up by the tail, or try to put him in a cage, he'll run in and out of the house all day long. Let's give him something to eat."

They gave him a little piece of raw meat. Rikki-tikki liked it immensely, and when it was finished he went out into the **veranda** and sat in the sunshine and fluffed up his fur to make it dry to the roots. Then he felt better.

"There are more things to find out about in this house," he said to himself, "than all my family could find out in all their lives. I shall certainly stay and find out."

He spent all that day roaming over the house. He nearly drowned himself in the bathtub, put his nose into

veranda a usually covered open gallery or long porch outside a building the ink on a writing table, and burned it on the end of the big man's cigar, for he climbed up in the big man's lap to see how writing was done. At nightfall he ran into Teddy's nursery to watch how kerosene lamps were lighted, and when Teddy went to bed Rikki-tikki climbed up too.

But he was a restless companion, because he had to get up and attend to every noise all through the night, and find out what made it. Teddy's mother and father came in, the last thing, to look at their boy, and Rikki-tikki was awake on the pillow.

"I don't like that," said Teddy's mother. "He may bite the child."

"He'll do no such thing," said the father. "Teddy's safer with that little beast than if he had a bloodhound to watch him. If a snake came into the nursery now—"

But Teddy's mother wouldn't think of anything so awful.

Early in the morning Rikki-tikki came to early breakfast in the veranda riding on Teddy's shoulder, and they gave him banana and some boiled egg. He sat on all their laps one after the other, because every well-brought-up mongoose always hopes to be a house mongoose some day and have rooms to run about in. And Rikki-tikki's mother, who used to live in the general's house at Segowlee, had carefully told Rikki what to do.

Then Rikki-tikki went out into the garden to see what was to be seen. It was a large garden, only half

cultivated, with rose bushes as big as **summerhouses**, lime and orange trees, clumps of bamboos, and thickets of high grass.

Rikki-tikki licked his lips. "This is a splendid hunting ground," he said, and his tail grew bottle-brushy at the thought of it. He scuttled up and down the garden, snuffing here and there till he heard very sorrowful voices in a thorn-bush.

It was Darzee the Tailorbird and his wife. They had made a beautiful nest by pulling two big leaves together and stitching them up the edges, and had filled the hollow with cotton and downy fluff. The nest swayed to and fro, as they sat on the rim and cried.

"What is the matter?" asked Rikki-tikki.

"We are very miserable," said Darzee. "One of our babies fell out of the nest yesterday and Nag ate him."

"Hmm!" said Rikki-tikki, "that is very sad—but I am a stranger here. Who is Nag?"

Darzee and his wife only cowered down in the nest without answering, for from the thick grass at the foot of the bush there came a low hiss—a horrid cold sound that made Rikki-tikki jump back two clear feet. Then inch by

....

cultivated planted, as with crops, trees, shrubs, or flowers
summerhouses covered structures in a park or garden that provide shade and places to sit

inch out of the grass rose up the head and spread hood of Nag, the big black cobra, and he was five feet long from tongue to tail. When he had lifted one-third of himself clear of the ground, he stayed balancing to and fro exactly as a dandelion tuft balances in the wind, and he looked at Rikki-tikki with the wicked snake's eyes that never change their expression, whatever the snake may be thinking of.

"Who is Nag?" said he. "*I* am Nag. Look, and be afraid!"

He spread out his hood more than ever, and Rikki-tikki saw the spectacle-mark on the back of it that looks exactly like the eye part of a hook-and-eye fastening. He was afraid for the minute, but it is impossible for a mongoose to stay frightened for any length of time. And, though Rikki-tikki had never met a live cobra before, his mother had fed him on dead ones. He knew that a grown mongoose's business in life was to fight and eat snakes. Nag knew that too and, at the bottom of his cold heart, he was afraid.

"Well," said Rikki-tikki, and his tail began to fluff up again, "marks or no marks, do you think it is right for you to eat fledglings out of a nest?"

Nag was thinking to himself, and watching the least little movement in the grass behind Rikki-tikki. He knew that mongooses in the garden meant death sooner or later for him and his family, but he wanted to get Rikki-tikki off his guard. So he dropped his head a little, and put it on one side.

"Let us talk," he said. "You eat eggs. Why shouldn't I eat birds?"

"Behind you! Look behind you!" sang Darzee.

Rikki-tikki knew better than to waste time in staring. He jumped up in the air as high as he could go, and just under him whizzed by the head of Nagaina, Nag's wicked wife. She had crept up behind him as he was talking, to make an end of him. He heard her savage hiss as the stroke missed.

He came down almost across her back, and if he had been an old mongoose he would have known that then was the time to break her back with one bite. But he was afraid of the terrible lashing return stroke of the cobra. He bit, indeed, but did not bite long enough, and he jumped clear of the whisking tail, leaving Nagaina torn and angry.

"Wicked, wicked Darzee!" said Nag, lashing up as high as he could reach toward the nest in the thornbush.

But Darzee had built it out of reach of snakes, and it only swayed to and fro.

Rikki-tikki felt his eyes growing red and hot (when a mongoose's eyes grow red, he is angry), and he sat back on his tail and hind legs like a little kangaroo, and looked all round him, and chattered with rage. But Nag and Nagaina had disappeared into the grass.

When a snake misses its stroke, it never says anything or gives any sign of what it means to do next. Rikki-tikki did not care to follow them, for he did not feel sure that he could manage two snakes at once. So he trotted off to the gravel path near the house, and sat down to think. It was a serious matter for him.

Rikki-tikki knew he was a young mongoose, and it made him all the more pleased to think that he had managed to escape a blow from behind. It gave him confidence in himself, and when Teddy came running down the path, Rikki-tikki was ready to be petted.

But just as Teddy was stooping, something wriggled a little in the dust, and a tiny voice said, "Be careful. I am Death!"

It was Karait, the dusty brown snakeling that lies on the dusty earth, and his bite is as dangerous as the cobra's. But he is so small that nobody thinks of him, and so he does more harm to people.

Rikki-tikki's eyes grew red again, and he danced up to Karait with the peculiar rocking, swaying motion that he had inherited from his family. If Rikki-tikki had only known, he was doing a much more dangerous thing than fighting Nag, for Karait is so small, and can turn so quickly, that unless Rikki bit him close to the back of the head, he would get the return stroke in his eye or his lip.

But Rikki did not know. His eyes were all red, and he rocked back and forth, looking for a good place to hold. Karait struck out. Rikki jumped sideways and tried to run in, but the wicked little dusty gray head lashed within a fraction of his shoulder, and he had to jump over the body, and the head followed his heels close.

Teddy shouted to the house, "Oh, look here! Our mongoose is killing a snake." Rikki-tikki heard a scream from Teddy's mother. Teddy's father ran out with a stick, but by the time he came up, Karait had lunged out once too far, and Rikki-tikki had sprung, jumped on the snake's back, dropped his head far between his forelegs, bitten as high up the back as he could get hold, and rolled away.

That bite **paralyzed** Karait. Rikki-tikki was just going to eat him up from the tail, after the custom of his family at dinner, when he remembered that a full meal makes

....

paralyzed made powerless or unable to move

a slow mongoose, and if he wanted all his strength and quickness ready, he must keep himself thin.

He went away for a dust bath under the castor-oil bushes, while Teddy's father beat the dead Karait.

"What is the use of that?" thought Rikki-tikki. "I have settled it all."

And then Teddy's mother picked him up from the dust and hugged him, crying that he had saved Teddy from death, and Teddy's father said that he was a **providence**, and Teddy looked on with big scared eyes. Rikki-tikki was rather amused at all the fuss, which, of course, he did not understand. Teddy's mother might just as well have petted Teddy for playing in the dust. Rikki was thoroughly enjoying himself.

That night at dinner, walking to and fro among the glasses on the table, he might have stuffed himself with nice things. But he remembered Nag and Nagaina, and though it was very pleasant to be patted and petted by Teddy's mother, and to sit on Teddy's shoulder, his eyes would get red from time to time, and he would go off into his long war cry of "*Rikk-tikk-tikki-tikki-tchk!*"

Teddy carried him off to bed, and insisted on Rikki-tikki sleeping under his chin.

....

providence divine care, as from a creator or deity

As soon as Teddy was asleep, Rikki-tikki went off for his nightly walk round the house. In the dark he ran up against Chuchundra the Muskrat, creeping around by the wall. Chuchundra is a broken-hearted little beast. He whimpers and cheeps all the night, trying to make up his mind to run into the middle of the room. But he never gets there.

"Don't kill me," said Chuchundra, almost weeping. "Rikki-tikki, don't kill me!"

"Do you think a snake-killer kills muskrats?" said Rikki-tikki scornfully.

"Those who kill snakes get killed by snakes," said Chuchundra, more sorrowfully than ever. "And how am I to be sure that Nag won't mistake me for you some dark night?"

"There's not the least danger," said Rikki-tikki. "But Nag is in the garden, and you don't go there."

"My cousin Chua the Rat told me—" said Chuchundra, and then he stopped.

"Told you what?"

"Hush! Nag is everywhere, Rikki-tikki. You should have talked to Chua in the garden."

"I didn't—so you must tell me. Quick, Chuchundra, or I'll bite you!"

Chuchundra sat down and cried till the tears rolled off his whiskers. "I am a very poor man," he sobbed. "I never had spirit enough to run out into the middle of the room. Hush! Can't you *hear*, Rikki-tikki?"

Rikki-tikki listened. The house was as still as still, but he thought he could just catch the faintest *scratch-scratch* in the world—a noise as faint as that of a wasp walking on a windowpane—the dry scratch of a snake's scales on brickwork.

"That's Nag or Nagaina," he said to himself, "and he is crawling into the bathroom sluice. You're right, Chuchundra. I should have talked to Chua."

He stole off to Teddy's bathroom, but there was nothing there, and then to Teddy's mother's bathroom. At the bottom of the smooth plaster wall there was a brick pulled out to make a sluice for the bath water. As Rikki-tikki stole in, he heard Nag and Nagaina whispering together outside in the moonlight.

"When the house is emptied of people," said Nagaina to her husband, "he will have to go away, and then the garden will be our own again. Go in quietly, and remember that the big man who killed Karait is the first one to bite. Then come out and tell me, and we will hunt for Rikki-tikki together."

"But are you sure that there is anything to be gained by killing the people?" said Nag.

"Everything. When there were no people in the bungalow, did we have any mongoose in the garden? So long as the bungalow is empty, we are king and queen of the garden. And remember that as soon as our eggs in the melon bed hatch (as they may tomorrow), our children will need room and quiet."

"I had not thought of that," said Nag. "I will go, but there is no need that we should hunt for Rikki-tikki afterward. I will kill the big man and his wife, and the child if I can, and come away quietly. Then the bungalow will be empty, and Rikki-tikki will go."

Rikki-tikki tingled all over with rage and hatred at this, and then Nag's head came through the sluice, and his five feet of cold body followed it. Angry as he was, Rikki-tikki was very frightened as he saw the size of the big cobra. Nag coiled himself up, raised his head, and looked into the bathroom in the dark. Rikki could see his eyes glitter.

"Now, if I kill him here, Nagaina will know. And if I fight him on the open floor, the odds are in his favor. What am I to do?" said Rikki-tikki-tavi.

Nag waved to and fro, and then Rikki-tikki heard him drinking from the biggest water jar that was used to fill the bath.

"When Karait was killed," said the snake, "the big man had a stick. He may have that stick still, but when he comes in to bathe in the morning he will not have a stick. I shall wait here till he comes. Nagaina—do you hear me? I shall wait here in the cool till daytime."

There was no answer from outside, so Rikki-tikki knew Nagaina had gone away. Nag coiled himself down, coil by coil, round the bulge at the bottom of the water jar, and Rikki-tikki stayed still as death. After an hour he began to move, muscle by muscle, toward the jar. Nag was asleep, and Rikki-tikki looked at his big back, wondering which would be the best place for a good hold.

"If I don't break his back at the first jump," said Rikki, "he can still fight. And if he fights—O Rikki!" He looked at the thickness of the neck below the hood, but that was too much for him. And a bite near the tail would only make Nag savage.

"It must be the head," he said at last, "the head above the hood. And, when I am once there, I must not let go."

Then he jumped. The head was lying a little clear of the water jar, under the curve of it. As his teeth met, Rikki braced his back against the bulge of the red earthenware to hold down the head.

Then he was battered to and fro as a rat is shaken by a dog—to and fro on the floor, up and down, and around

in great circles. His eyes were red
and he held on as the body whipped
over the floor, upsetting the tin dipper and
the soap dish and the brush, and banged against the
side of the bath. As he held, he closed his jaws tighter
and tighter, for he was sure he would be banged to
death, and, for the honor of his family, he preferred to
be found with his teeth locked. He was dizzy, aching,
and felt shaken to pieces when something went off like
a thunderclap just behind him. A hot wind knocked him
senseless and red fire singed his fur. The big man had
been wakened by the noise, and had fired both barrels of
a shotgun into Nag just behind the hood.

Rikki-tikki held on with his eyes shut, for now he was quite sure he was dead. But the head did not move, and the big man picked him up and said, "It's the mongoose again, Alice. The little chap has saved our lives now."

Then Teddy's mother came in with a very white face, and saw what was left of Nag. Rikki-tikki dragged himself to Teddy's bedroom and spent half the rest of the night shaking himself tenderly to find out whether he really was broken into forty pieces, as he fancied.

When morning came he was very stiff, but well pleased with his doings. "Now I have Nagaina to settle with, and she will be worse than five Nags, and there's no knowing when the eggs she spoke of will hatch. Goodness! I must go and see Darzee," he said.

Without waiting for breakfast, Rikki-tikki ran to the thornbush where Darzee was singing a song of triumph at the top of his voice. The news of Nag's death was all over the garden, for the sweeper had thrown the body on the rubbish heap.

"Oh, you stupid tuft of feathers!" said Rikki-tikki angrily. "Is this the time to sing?"

"Nag is dead—is dead—is dead!" sang Darzee. "The valiant Rikki-tikki caught him by the head and held fast. The big man brought the bang-stick, and Nag fell in two pieces! He will never eat my babies again."

"All that's true enough. But where's Nagaina?" said Rikki-tikki, looking carefully round him.

"Nagaina came to the bathroom sluice and called for Nag," Darzee went on, "and Nag came out on the end of a stick—the sweeper picked him up on the end of a stick and threw him upon the rubbish heap. Let us sing about the great, the red-eyed Rikki-tikki!" And Darzee filled his throat and sang.

"If I could get up to your nest, I'd roll your babies out!" said Rikki-tikki. "You don't know when to do the right thing at the right time. You're safe enough in your nest there, but it's war for me down here. Stop singing a minute, Darzee."

"For the great, the beautiful Rikki-tikki's sake I will stop," said Darzee. "What is it, O Killer of the terrible Nag?"

"Where is Nagaina, for the third time?"

"On the rubbish heap by the stables, mourning for Nag. Great is Rikki-tikki with the white teeth."

"Bother my white teeth! Have you ever heard where she keeps her eggs?"

"In the melon bed, on the end nearest the wall, where the sun strikes nearly all day. She hid them there weeks ago."

"And you never thought it worthwhile to tell me? The end nearest the wall, you said?"

"Rikki-tikki, you are not going to eat her eggs?"

"Not eat exactly, no. Darzee, if you have a grain of sense you will fly off to the stables and pretend that your wing is broken, and let Nagaina chase you away to this bush. I must get to the melon bed, and if I went there now she'd see me."

Darzee was a feather-brained little fellow who could never hold more than one idea at a time in his head. And just because he knew that Nagaina's children were born in eggs like his own, he didn't think at first that it was fair to kill them. But his wife was a sensible bird, and she knew that cobra's eggs meant young cobras later on. So she flew off from the nest, and left Darzee to keep the babies warm, and continue his song about the death of Nag. Darzee was very like a man in some ways.

She fluttered in front of Nagaina by the rubbish heap and cried out, "Oh, my wing is broken! The boy in the house threw a stone at me and broke it." Then she fluttered more desperately than ever.

Nagaina lifted up her head and hissed, "You warned Rikki-tikki when I would have killed him. Indeed and truly, you've chosen a bad place to be lame in." And she moved toward Darzee's wife, slipping along over the dust.

"The boy broke it with a stone!" shrieked Darzee's wife.

"Well! It may be some consolation to you when you're dead to know that before night the boy in the house will lie very still. What is the use of running away? I am sure to catch you. Little fool, look at me!"

Darzee's wife knew better than to do that, for a bird who looks at a snake's eyes gets so frightened that she cannot move. Darzee's wife fluttered on, piping sorrowfully, and never leaving the ground. Nagaina quickened her pace.

Rikki-tikki heard them going up the path from the stables, and he raced for the end of the melon patch near the wall. There, in the warm litter above the melons, very **cunningly** hidden, he found twenty-five eggs, about the size of a bantam's eggs, but with whitish skin instead of shell.

"I was not a day too soon," he said, for he could see the baby cobras curled up inside the skin, and he knew that the minute they were hatched they could each kill a man or a mongoose. He bit off the tops of the eggs as fast as he could, taking care to crush the young cobras, and turned over the litter from time to time to see whether he had missed any. At last there were only three eggs left, and Rikki-tikki began to chuckle to himself, when he heard Darzee's wife screaming:

"Rikki-tikki, I led Nagaina toward the house, and she has gone into the veranda, and—oh, come quickly—she means killing!"

....

cunningly cleverly, slyly, or sneakily

Rikki-tikki smashed two eggs, and tumbled backward down the melon bed with the third egg in his mouth, and scuttled to the veranda as hard as he could put foot to the ground. Teddy and his mother and father were there at early breakfast, but Rikki-tikki saw that they were not eating anything. They sat stone still, and their faces were white. Nagaina was coiled up by Teddy's chair, within easy striking distance of Teddy's bare leg, and she was swaying to and fro, singing a song of triumph.

"Son of the big man that killed Nag," she hissed, "stay still. I am not ready yet. Wait a little. Keep very still, all you three! If you move I strike, and if you do not move I strike. Oh, foolish people, who killed my Nag!"

Teddy's eyes were fixed on his father, and all his father could do was to whisper, "Sit still, Teddy. You mustn't move. Teddy, keep still."

Then Rikki-tikki came up and cried, "Turn round, Nagaina. Turn and fight!"

"All in good time," said she, without moving her eyes. "I will deal with you presently. Look at your friends, Rikki-tikki. They are still and white. They are afraid. They dare not move, and if you come a step nearer I strike."

"Look at your eggs," said Rikki-tikki, "in the melon bed near the wall. Go and look, Nagaina!"

The big snake turned half around, and saw the egg on the veranda. "Ahh! Give it to me," she said.

Rikki-tikki put his paws one on each side of the egg, and his eyes were blood red. "What price for a snake's egg? For a young cobra? For a young king cobra? For the last—the very last of the brood? The ants are eating all the others down by the melon bed."

Nagaina spun clear round, forgetting everything for the sake of the one egg. Rikki-tikki saw Teddy's father shoot out a big hand, catch Teddy by the shoulder, and drag him across the little table with the teacups, safe and out of reach of Nagaina.

"Tricked! Tricked! Tricked! *Rikk-tck-tck*!" chuckled Rikki-tikki. "The boy is safe, and it was I—I—I that caught Nag by the hood last night in the bathroom." Then he began to jump up and down, all four feet together, his head close to the floor. "He threw me to and fro, but he could not shake me off. He was dead before the big man blew him in two. I did it! *Rikki-tikki-tck-tck*! Come then, Nagaina. Come and fight with me."

Nagaina saw that she had lost her chance of killing Teddy, and the egg lay between Rikki-tikki's paws. "Give me the egg, Rikki-tikki. Give me the last of my eggs, and I will go away and never come back," she said, lowering her hood.

"Yes, you will go away, and you will never come back. For you will go to the rubbish heap with Nag. Fight! The big man has gone for his gun! Fight!"

Rikki-tikki was bounding all round Nagaina, keeping just out of reach of her stroke, his little eyes like hot coals. Nagaina gathered herself together like a watch spring and flung out at him. Rikki-tikki jumped up and backward. Again and again and again she struck. Then Rikki-tikki danced in a circle to get behind her, and Nagaina spun round to keep her head to his head, so that the rustle of her tail on the floor sounded like dry leaves blown along by the wind.

He had forgotten the egg. It still lay on the veranda, and Nagaina came nearer and nearer to it, till at last, while Rikki-tikki was drawing breath, she caught it in her mouth, turned to the veranda steps, and flew like an arrow down the path, with Rikki-tikki behind her. When the cobra runs for her life, she goes like a whiplash flicked across a horse's neck.

Rikki-tikki knew that he must catch her, or all the trouble would begin again. She headed straight for the long grass by the thornbush, and as he was running Rikki-tikki heard Darzee still singing his foolish little song of triumph.

But Darzee's wife was wiser. She flew off her nest as Nagaina came along, and flapped her wings about Nagaina's head. If Darzee had helped they might have turned her, but Nagaina only lowered her hood and went on. Still, the instant's delay brought Rikki-tikki up to her, and as she plunged into the rathole where she and Nag used to live, his little white teeth were clenched on her tail, and he went down with her—and very few mongooses, however wise and old they may be, care to follow a cobra into its hole.

It was dark in the hole, and Rikki-tikki never knew when it might open out and give Nagaina room to turn and strike at him. He held on savagely and stuck out his feet to act as brakes on the dark slope of the hot, moist earth.

Then the grass by the mouth of the hole stopped waving, and Darzee said, "It is all over with Rikki-tikki! We must sing his death song. Valiant Rikki-tikki is dead! For Nagaina will surely kill him underground."

So he sang a very mournful song that he made up on the spur of the minute, and just as he got to the most touching part, the grass quivered again, and Rikki-tikki, covered with dirt, dragged himself out of the hole leg by leg, licking his whiskers. Darzee stopped with a little shout. Rikki-tikki shook some of the dust out of his fur and sneezed. "It is all over," he said. "Nagaina will never come out again." And the red ants that live between the grass stems heard him, and began to troop down one after another to see if he had spoken the truth.

Rikki-tikki curled himself up in the grass and slept where he was—slept and slept till it was late in the afternoon, for he had done a hard day's work.

"Now," he said, when he awoke, "I will go back to the house. Tell the Coppersmith, Darzee, and he will tell the garden that Nagaina is dead."

The Coppersmith is a bird who makes a noise exactly like the beating of a little hammer on a copper pot. And the reason he is always making it is because he is the town crier to every Indian garden, and tells all the news to everybody who cares to listen. As Rikki-tikki went up the path, he heard his "attention" notes like a tiny dinner gong, and then the steady *"Ding-dong-tock! Nag is dead— dong!* Nagaina is dead! *Ding-dong-tock!"* That set all the birds in the garden singing, and the frogs croaking, for Nag and Nagaina used to eat frogs as well as little birds.

When Rikki got to the house, Teddy and Teddy's mother and Teddy's father came out and almost cried over him. And that night he ate all that was given him till he could eat no more, and went to bed on Teddy's shoulder, where Teddy's mother saw him when she came to look late at night.

"He saved our lives and Teddy's life," she said to her husband. "Just think, he saved all our lives."

Rikki-tikki woke up with a jump, for the mongooses are light sleepers.

"Oh, it's you," said he. "What are you bothering for? All the cobras are dead. And if they weren't, I'm here."

Rikki-tikki had a right to be proud of himself. But he did not grow too proud, and he kept that garden as a mongoose should keep it, with tooth and jump and spring and bite, till never a cobra dared show its head inside the walls.

Darzee's Chant

(Sung in honor of Rikki-tikki-tavi)

Singer and tailor am I—
   Doubled the joys that I know—
Proud of my lilt to the sky,
   Proud of the house that I sew—
Over and under, so weave I my music—so weave I
   the house that I sew.

Sing to your fledglings again,
   Mother, O lift up your head!
Evil that plagued us is slain,
   Death in the garden lies dead.
Terror that hid in the roses is impotent—flung on
   the dunghill and dead!

Who has delivered us, who?
   Tell me his nest and his name.
Rikki, the valiant, the true,
   Tikki, with eyeballs of flame,
Rikk-tikki-tikki, the ivory-fanged, the hunter with
   eyeballs of flame!

Give him the Thanks of the Birds,
  Bowing with tail feathers spread!
Praise him with nightingale words—
  Nay, I will praise him instead.
Hear! I will sing you the praise of the bottle-tailed
  Rikki, with eyeballs of red!

(Here Rikki-tikki interrupted, so the rest of the song is lost.)

Men and Women
of Character

Ibrahim

In July 2003, I was a combat **medic** in the 101st Airborne Infantry division and stationed close to Kirkuk, Iraq. This was near the start of the war, but, luckily for me and my unit, things were mostly quiet then. The groups that called Kirkuk home—Kurds, Arabs, Turkmen—hadn't yet started fighting one another for control of the city.

One Wednesday afternoon, after a patrol, we were returning to the base. I was happy because I was going to call my daughter, Alice, that night. Alice was just seven, and my being away was tough on her. Every phone call meant a lot.

So Alice was on my mind when, ten kilometers from the base, I saw something—or, rather, someone. On the roadside was a boy of about five. He was alone, and I didn't know if others had seen him. I signaled to Lieutenant Ramirez.

"I saw," he said. "What do you think, Bolger?"

---

medic also *corpsman*, in the military, one trained to give first aid an some medical treatment

"I think he's lost," I said. "And who knows how he got here. There's nothing around for miles."

He nodded and ordered our Humvee to stop. We looked again. The boy was filthy and very thin. I opened the door, and Lieutenant Ramirez scanned the **perimeter**. Nothing moved. His face was as serious as stone.

"Be careful," he said.

I understood. Lieutenant Ramirez was a good man, but he couldn't know whether the enemy might use the boy as bait to lure us into an **ambush**. I got out of the Humvee.

It wasn't an ambush. The boy stood still as I approached, which was a relief. I worried I might scare him and have to chase him, which would scare him more. But he stayed put, and I knelt. I smiled. We didn't have a **translator** with us, so I did my best.

"*Um?*" I said, which means "mother" in Arabic.

The boy shook his head. I wondered if he thought I was saying I was his mother. So I touched my chest and said my name.

"Mary," I repeated, before gently touching his chest.

"Ibrahim," he said.

---

perimeter the outermost boundary of an area

ambush a surprise attack from a hidden position

translator one who translates, that is, relates in one's own language words spoken or written in another

I smiled again. I said his name twice and tapped his chest to show I understood. Then I mimed eating food, my hands to my lips. Ibrahim again shook his head.

I reached into my pack and pulled out a granola bar. Alice and my husband had sent it in their latest care package. I handed the bar to Ibrahim. Then I unscrewed the cap of my canteen and placed it at his feet.

As he ate and drank, I returned to the Humvee. Lieutenant Ramirez stood outside it.

"I know what you're gonna say, Bolger. I can't **authorize** it."

"So we'll leave him?" I asked. "What'll happen then, sir?"

"There could be hundreds of kids in his situation."

....

authorize to permit by way of recognized or proper procedure

"We didn't find them," I said. "We found him."

He sighed. I continued: "If we leave him, he could get hit by a car. He could starve. Striped hyena live out here. We're here to help these people, right, sir?"

Again, Lieutenant Ramirez was a good man. Minutes later, we were bumping along in the Humvee, Ibrahim seated on my lap. He ate two more granola bars and drank all the water in my canteen.

Back at the base, we cleaned Ibrahim up and our translator, Malik, spoke to him. Malik learned that Ibrahim had crawled into the back of a truck two days earlier and fallen asleep. When he woke, he was in the city. But when Malik asked where Ibrahim lived, Ibrahim didn't know. We were stumped. We left Malik to eat dinner in the chow hall, and Ibrahim gobbled up every bite.

After dinner, I called Alice. Again, Ibrahim came with me. He trusted me, and as I talked to Alice, I told her about his situation. Alice had an idea.

"Have him draw a picture of where he lives," she said.

It sounds crazy, right? A seven-year-old suggesting a five-year-old draw a picture to help adults learn something? Maybe it was crazy. But it worked.

With Malik directing him, Ibrahim drew his hometown. As Ibrahim drew, Malik asked questions: Is that a river? Are those mountains? Is that a bridge? That's a soccer stadium, right?

Together, we figured out that Ibrahim was likely from Taqtaq, about 60 kilometers north. Lieutenant Ramirez arranged for us to be part of a **convoy** traveling there two days later. There was hope.

For the next 48 hours, Ibrahim and I were **inseparable**. We ate snacks. We played simple card games. He even held my hand when we walked across the base just like Alice did at home. When we left for Taqtaq on Friday, Ibrahim buckled in next to me, my heart was in my throat.

What if we were wrong? What if something had happened to Ibrahim's parents? I put these fears out of my mind, and as we approached the bridge over the Little Zab River, Ibrahim grew excited. We were in the right place.

We drove on. Malik translated, and Ibrahim pointed out things he recognized. We tried to zero in on where he lived, but it wasn't easy. Ibrahim didn't know his address, and we couldn't find some of the landmarks he described.

Then we got lucky. On a quiet block, one I thought we'd been on several times, Ibrahim shouted. Then he nearly jumped out of his seat. He pointed excitedly, his finger banging on the Humvee's window.

"Um! Um!"

....

convoy a protective escort of, for example, military vehicles or ships
inseparable always together; not able to be apart

Mother! Mother!

We didn't need Malik to translate that. We stopped and Ibrahim got out and sprinted down the street, still shouting. Ahead, a woman about my age walked in the opposite direction. When she heard Ibrahim's voice, she turned. I will never forget the look on her face.

In a flash, Ibrahim was in her arms. She smiled and she thanked God. She kissed him and kissed him and kissed him. She cried, and so did I. Then Ibrahim took his mother by the hand and led her to me. I smiled through my tears, and she wrapped me in a hug.

"Um Mary," Ibrahim told her again and again. "Um Mary. Um Mary."

Maria Gonzalez, Modern Hero

It's tough being nine, going on ten. It's especially tough being nine, going on ten, while short and skinny. And it's super-especially tough being nine, going on ten, while short and skinny and in a wheelchair. But that's how it was for Maria Gonzalez.

Most of the time, Maria stayed upbeat. She had lots of friends. She sang in the choir, and she was very bright. She even played in a wheelchair basketball league. But some days, Maria felt blue. Sometimes, life felt unfair. And that's when she turned to her favorite stories to cheer her up.

Maria loved to read the **myths** of ancient Greece and Rome. She knew all about the labors of Hercules. She thrilled to the adventures of Bellerophon and his winged horse, Pegasus. And she cried when Icarus's pride led him to fly too high on his wax wings. Yet of all the myths, Maria's favorites were those about Athena.

....

myths ancient traditional stories, involving gods, goddesses, and magic, that served to explain beliefs, practices, or nature

Athena was the Greek goddess of wisdom and heroism, so she was smart and tough. But, like all the Olympian gods, Athena wasn't perfect. She could be stubborn and sometimes lost her temper. But while these flaws might have made Athena less appealing to some, they made Maria like her even more.

Because Maria had a stubborn streak, too. She also had a **short fuse**. So it was easy to understand why Maria often imagined herself as Athena, overcoming everything to save the day with daring and intelligence. Indeed, Maria was daydreaming about Athena one fateful afternoon when her world suddenly felt like it was ripped from the pages of one of her favorite stories.

....

short fuse quick temper

Maria was on Fawn Street near the library when someone yelled. She turned and saw, down the block, a young man with blond hair. He wore a blue shirt and was running toward her. Behind him, a woman in a red coat gave chase.

"Stop!" the woman shouted. "Thief!"

Maria could see, in the man's hand, a leather purse. The woman was not going to catch him, and nobody else was around. As the thief turned onto Barkley Avenue, Maria knew she had to act.

Barkley Avenue sloped down from Fawn Street, and it dead-ended at the Hanley River. A jogging trail lined the river, which was shaded by large oak trees. As the thief sprinted down Barkley Avenue, Maria rolled her chair to the top of the hill.

She thought about the heroes and **heroines** she loved. She thought about the woman whose purse had been stolen. She took a deep breath. Then she pushed her wheelchair forward.

The wind blew back Maria's hair. The wheels of her chair hummed as they spun. She rolled faster and faster down the hill. She was Bellerophon. Her chair was Pegasus. She felt like she was flying, and it was **exhilarating**.

----

heroines in myth, women, often of divine heritage, with great and perhaps magical strength and ability; in literature or drama, female main characters
exhilarating joyfully exciting

Maria gained on the thief. His shirt had a picture of a deer on the back. The deer's massive antlers made Maria think of the **Ceryneian Hind**, which was so fast that Hercules chased it for a full year before capturing it. Maria hoped this chase would be much shorter.

....

Ceryneian Hind also the Golden Hind, in mythology, a huge female deer, sacred pet of Artemis, goddess of the hunt and wild animals

She hollered, "Give back the purse!"

But the man looked over his shoulder, sneered, and sprinted even faster. Maria **grimaced**. This thief didn't think the short, skinny nine-year-old in the wheelchair could catch him. She grew angry and her stubbornness kicked in. She pushed her chair harder.

As they neared the bottom of the hill, Maria was just behind the man. Ahead was the jogging trail, an oak tree, and the river. When the man didn't turn, Maria thought he might dive into the water and swim across the Hanley. She couldn't let that happen.

So, when the man's leg kicked up behind him as he ran, Maria slapped his foot. That threw him off balance and he stumbled. He fell and slid across the jogging trail, stopping at the base of the oak.

Meanwhile, Maria miraculously managed to skid to a stop without tipping over. Now she sat between the thief and the river. If he made a break for the water, she'd block him.

The man had a different plan, though. Purse in hand, he scrambled up the oak and made his way onto a long limb above. The limb stretched far out over the river—so far that the leaves at the far end hung over the opposite bank.

---

grimaced distorted one's face, or made a facial expression, to show disapproval, disgust, or anger

Maria understood now. He was going to go out on the limb as far as possible and jump to the other side of the water. But the limb grew thinner the farther he went, and it bent lower. He was ten feet over the water, and Maria saw fear in the man's eyes. She understood that, too.

"You can't swim," she said.

He didn't respond, but he didn't have to. Maria knew she was right. A thought came to her.

"Do you know the story of Icarus?"

The man looked at her. The limb groaned under his weight.

"Wax wings?" he said. "He flies too close to the sun, and they melt."

"Because he thinks he can do what he's already been told not to," Maria said.

The man stopped. The limb swayed in the breeze. There was a cracking sound.

"It's not worth your life," Maria said.

The man waited a moment. At last, he turned and inched back to the trunk of the oak. He was just climbing down when the police cruiser arrived, lights flashing and siren howling. When he reached the ground again, a police officer with a bushy mustache slapped handcuffs on him.

Once the man was in the back of the squad car, the police officer came over to Maria. He had kind eyes, and his bushy mustache twitched as he talked.

"Thank you for your help, young lady" he began. "You stopped this crime all by yourself. That must've been a Herculean effort!"

"Nah," Maria replied with a wink. "It was more like an Athenian one."

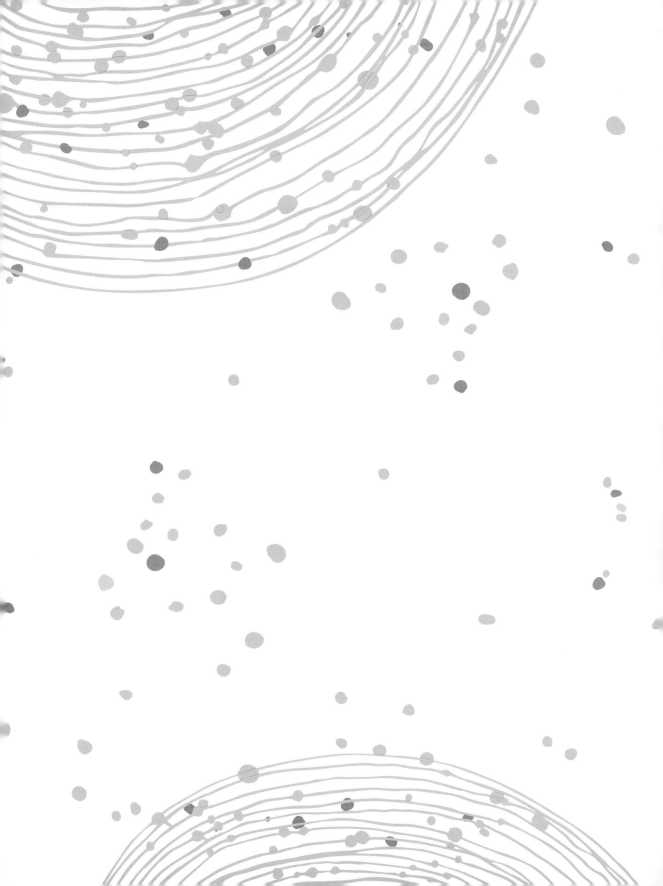

Grace

Grace sits on her bed, her shoulders slumped, and she stares at the tiny dark spots on her gray shorts. They are the places where her tears have landed, and more appear every moment. The light from the setting sun outside pours through the windows and casts her bedroom in a gloomy orange tint. She wipes her eyes with a tissue.

The cat clock on Grace's wall ticks and tocks as the second hand inches around its circuit. It is 5:50. She has ten minutes.

At six o'clock, Mom will return from work. Then Dad will tell her what happened. And Grace will hear Mom's feet on the stairs, see her bedroom door open, and feel those dreaded words pierce her like an arrow to the heart: Grace Mei Lu.

Mom only uses Grace's full name when she's really disappointed. And she doesn't yell it. She speaks it very slowly, as if every letter weighs a thousand pounds, like pronouncing each syllable exhausts her.

Grace checks the clock again: 5:51.

Now she imagines being able to make time go backward. She pictures the day unfolding in reverse and thinks how nice that would be. She sighs and stares at the ceiling.

The afternoon began so well. Grace and Karen kicked the soccer ball, climbed trees, and drew pictures on the porch. At four o'clock, Dad even let them have chocolate-covered pretzels for a snack and jokingly made them swear not to tell Mom.

"Don't rat me out to Mom, girls," Dad said with a wink. "I don't want to face her wrath!"

Grace and Karen both pinky-promised that they'd never tell Mom. Then they went down to the basement to play. Dad stayed upstairs to make dinner. As Grace and Karen descended the steps, they heard him whistling to himself.

"Grace, play nicely with Karen," he called from the kitchen. "And don't wreck the basement more than it already is!"

The Lu basement looked like a toy store that had been shaken and turned upside down. Scattered everywhere were board games and sports equipment, art supplies and musical instruments, model planes and action figures. Grace and Karen could have played almost anything and nothing bad would have happened. But Grace spotted her skateboard and Karen's jump rope, and she got an idea.

"Let's make a **catapult**," Grace suggested.

Karen agreed, mostly because she worshipped her big sister, and the girls began building. For the next hour, they were all business and the time flew by. Grace always enjoyed these types of projects and took them seriously. Whatever she made, she wanted it to work. Just like Mom, Dad always said, Grace was an engineer at heart.

By 5:15, their catapult was complete. Granted, it looked like a Frankenstein's monster version of a catapult—the skateboard and a tennis racket here, the jump rope and a toy magic wand there—but it did its job. When Grace loaded a tennis ball onto the

....

catapult a device for hurling objects

launcher and released the lever, a plastic microphone stand, the ball arced beautifully across the room and bounced off the far wall.

Grace smiled and reset the catapult for a second launch with a softball. When that succeeded, she loaded a box of crayons and watched it soar across the basement, too. It crashed into the wall with a thud, though, and the door to the basement opened.

"What're those noises?" Dad asked from upstairs. "Are you girls throwing things?"

Neither girl answered at first. Technically, they weren't throwing things. Technically, the catapult was launching things.

"No," Grace fibbed, and Dad mumbled something as he closed the door again.

Obviously, they should've stopped then. Clearly, Grace never should've loaded the catapult once more, this time with a cast-iron toy car. And certainly, it was a mistake for Grace to tell Karen to stand on the other side of the room and catch the car before it hit the wall so Dad wouldn't hear.

But **hindsight is 20/20**. Grace didn't stop. She loaded the catapult. She launched the car, and it hit Karen squarely in her left eye.

Then came the screaming. Then came the tears. Then came Grace lying that she didn't know how Karen got hurt and Dad sending Grace to her room.

Which is where she sits as the cat clock strikes six, and Mom arrives home. The room is darker now than it was ten minutes ago. The gloomy orange tint has given way to even bleaker gray shadows. There is a pit in her stomach as Grace hears Dad's muffled voice downstairs. Now Mom's feet are on the steps, and her door opens.

Grace braces herself, but the sound of her full name never comes. Instead, Mom comes and sits next to her. For a moment, the only sound is the ticking clock.

"When I was your age," Mom begins, "I built a **crane** with a wrecking ball hanging from it, using scrap wood

....

hindsight is 20/20 a saying that means that it's often clear what would have been the right thing to do, but it's too late now; literally, *hindsight* means thinking or looking back and *20/20 eyesight* means perfectly clear vision
crane a tall machine used for lifting and moving objects

that Grandpa kept in our garage and strong wire and his bowling ball. It took me hours. And when I tested it, I pulled the bowling ball back until the wire was taut and let go."

"What happened?" Grace asks.

"It worked. The crane was stable. The wire held. The bowling ball swung perfectly. I was very proud," Mom says, "until I realized Grandpa's car was in the way."

"Oh, no."

"Oh, yes. The ball smashed the taillight to bits. Grandpa heard the noise and came running."

"Did you get in trouble?" Grace asks.

"I did, but not because I built the crane. Grandpa liked that. No, I got in trouble because when he asked what happened, I lied and said I didn't know."

"Wasn't the crane with the bowling ball right there?" Grace says.

"I didn't say it was a good lie," Mom answers. "The point is that it's good to be creative and to experiment and to build. But you have to do it safely. You have to be careful. And you can't lie about what you're doing or what you've done."

"I know," Grace says. "I'm sorry."

"Now go apologize to Karen and Dad," Mom tells her. "Then you can take me down to the basement so I can see this awesome catapult you built."

Healthy and Safe

Elizabeth Blackwell
A Pioneering Physician

by Vanessa Wright

What do you want to be when you grow up? When six-year-old Elizabeth Blackwell was asked that question, she stuck out her chin and replied, "I don't know what I'm going to be. But I think that it will be something hard!"

The little girl was right. She grew up to become a doctor. That is hard enough. But Elizabeth Blackwell was not only a doctor. She was also a pioneer. That doesn't mean that she traveled west in a covered wagon. It means that she led the way for others by being the first to do something new and difficult.

As you will see, what she did turned out to be very hard to do—harder, perhaps, than she ever imagined.

Young Elizabeth Blackwell grasped the rail of the rolling ship. Her face was pale. Her legs wobbled as if they were made of jelly.

It was the year 1832, and the eleven-year-old girl had been seasick almost every day since she and her family had left England. But as she breathed in the fresh air, her eyes brightened. The sun brought color back to her cheeks.

"Bessie," called Elizabeth's father, striding across the deck, "are you all right?" Many of the passengers in first class had been seasick, and Samuel Blackwell was worried about his daughter.

"Yes, Papa," Elizabeth replied. "I feel better out here." Then she frowned. "Tell me, how many more days will it take us to reach America?"

"Not many," Mr. Blackwell said. "Don't worry, Bessie. Once we land in America, you'll run around and play as though you were never ill."

"It isn't me I'm worried about," said Elizabeth. "I'm just seasick. But the captain said that the people in steerage have cholera."

"Yes," said her father, "that's true."

"Oh, Papa," said Elizabeth, "it's dark and dirty down there. The people can't come up and stand in the sunlight. I heard the captain say that almost half of them have died. And there's no doctor to help them."

Mr. Blackwell looked in his daughter's eyes and asked, "What do you think should be done?"

"Someone needs to help them!" Elizabeth cried. "Papa, you always say that everyone is equal, whether they're black or white, men or women, rich or poor. So why should the poor people in steerage die while everyone on our deck stays healthy?"

"Bessie," said Mr. Blackwell gently, "on almost every long sea voyage, people come down with cholera."

Elizabeth gazed out over the sea. "Then there must be something causing people to get sick," she said. "If doctors could find out what it is, they could tell people about it, and teach them how to stay healthy. Then people wouldn't get sick in the first place."

The little girl turned to her father. "And I shall do it," she said firmly. "When I grow up, I will be a doctor. I will help anyone in need, and I will teach people how to stay healthy."

Mr. Blackwell nodded. "I believe you can, Bessie. I know you can."

But most people who lived during Elizabeth's time did not agree with Mr. Blackwell. They thought that when girls grew up, it was all right for them to be servants, or to work on farms or in factories. But women weren't allowed to become lawyers, bankers, or doctors, or to hold other jobs that were just for men.

Back then, girls received little education. They were

not allowed to go to good schools. Many girls did not go to school at all. "Why waste a good education on a girl?" people said. "After all, no woman can do a job as well as a man."

But Mr. Blackwell disagreed. He taught Elizabeth and his other children that all people should have equal rights. He believed that a woman could do a job as well as a man. He taught his daughters subjects that only boys learned in school, such as history and math. And he encouraged his daughters to be whatever they wanted to be.

Elizabeth wanted to be a doctor. She read all the books she could find. She studied with doctors to learn about the human body. She talked with scientists to learn how medicines are made and how they work.

Finally, Elizabeth decided to apply to medical school. Most people said, "A woman doctor—that's ridiculous!" Women were not supposed to go to college in Elizabeth's time. They certainly were not supposed to be doctors.

But Elizabeth was determined. She applied to 29 medical schools. Twenty-eight of the schools said no.

Then, on a crisp October day, she received a letter. Her fingers trembled as she opened the flap. As she read the message, her face lit up. Geneva Medical College, a small school in New York, had accepted her! "I will be a doctor," she cried, and ran inside to pack her bags.

But Elizabeth's struggle had just begun. Many of the students, teachers, and townspeople were shocked and angry when she arrived. Some students called her names. One teacher refused to let Elizabeth into his classroom. The townspeople stared at her and muttered rude things about her. Some children even chased her through the streets, screeching, "Doctor in petticoats! Doctor in petticoats!"

Elizabeth was frustrated, but she did not give up. As she walked to and from her classes, she recited the names of bones and muscles. She studied her books until her tallest candle melted into a puddle of wax. She quickly became the best student in her class. And through it all, she stayed calm and spoke kindly to everyone. Slowly, her courage and determination won the people's respect and friendship.

At last, the day came for Elizabeth to graduate. In the morning, she and her brother, Henry, slipped into the church where the ceremony would be held. When they arrived, many of the seats were already filled with curious women, whispering excitedly to each other. The two took their seats by the aisle.

As the graduates entered the church, the organist began to play. Elizabeth stood and walked to the front row of seats with her fellow classmates.

In groups of four, all the men were called up to receive their diplomas. Elizabeth was called up last of all, and alone. The president of the college took off his hat and presented her with her diploma.

Elizabeth bowed and turned to go back to her seat. Then, suddenly, she said to the president, "Sir, I thank you. By the help of the Most High, it shall be the effort of my life to shed honor upon your diploma."

Elizabeth bowed to the president of the college, and he bowed to her. The audience burst into applause. Then Dr. Elizabeth Blackwell took her seat with her fellow doctors at the front of the church. She had just become the first woman to graduate from a medical college—the first woman doctor.

After she graduated, Dr. Blackwell worked for a while in hospitals in France and England. In 1851, she returned to the United States. No hospital would hire her. So she bought a house, and there she took care of sick women and children.

She also wrote books that showed people how to stay healthy. She encouraged them to eat right and keep things clean. She also told people not to wait until they were very sick to go to a doctor. She called her teachings preventative medicine. She wanted to prevent disease, to stop it before it started. "Even better than curing ills is seeing that ills do not happen in the first place," she said.

Elizabeth had not forgotten the poor people on the ship that carried her to America so many years before. "Poor women and children need good hospitals, too," she thought. "I will build a place where they can come to get well."

She rented a room in one of the poorest neighborhoods in New York City. Trash was piled up in the front yard. The front door hung on one hinge and banged in the wind. Inside, the room was dirty and bare.

"Isn't there a nicer, cleaner place where we might start a hospital?" asked the women who were helping Elizabeth.

"No," Elizabeth replied. "Good health can start anywhere. And it is most needed right here."

She and her friends cleared the trash out of the yard.

They fixed the door. They cleaned and painted the little room, and tacked up pretty curtains. Caring families donated chairs, a desk, a table, and a cot.

Elizabeth put her heavy medical books on one shelf. She placed medicines and bandages on another. She polished her medical instruments and tucked them away in a drawer. Then she threw open the door of the clinic.

For many days, no one came. Then one morning, Elizabeth saw an old woman walking slowly toward the door. She held one arm tightly against her side. Her face was twisted with pain.

The old woman opened the door. She peered into the cheerful room. She saw only Elizabeth sitting at her desk. "Is there no doctor here?" she asked.

Elizabeth replied, "I am the doctor. Come in. I can help you."

Elizabeth helped the old woman get better. After a few days, the old woman returned, leading her sick grandchild by the hand. Behind her huddled a dozen more sick people.

Soon Elizabeth had a line of patients stretching down the block. Many of them had never visited a doctor in their lives. Elizabeth helped them get well. Then she visited their homes to teach them about healthy living. She also got help from a welcome friend—her sister, Emily Blackwell. Emily had just graduated from medical school. She, too, had become a doctor.

The sisters' little clinic grew to become the New York Infirmary for Indigent Women and Children. Here, Elizabeth also started the Women's Medical College to train more women to become doctors.

Following in the footsteps of Elizabeth Blackwell, thousands of women have become doctors. The determined little girl did indeed grow up to do "something hard." Looking back on her life, Dr. Blackwell said, "It is not easy to be a pioneer, but oh, it is fascinating! I would not trade one moment, even the worst moment, for all the riches in the world."

Excerpts from Elizabeth Blackwell's Autobiography

May 27.

— Called on Dr. Jackson (one of the oldest professors in Philadelphia), a small, bright-faced, grey-haired man, who looked up from his newspaper and saluted me with, 'Well, what is it? What do you want?' I told him I wanted to study medicine. He began to laugh, and asked me why. Then I detailed my plans. He became interested; said he would not give me an answer then; that there were great difficulties, but he did not know that they were insurmountable; he would let me know on Monday. I came home with a lighter heart, though I can hardly say I hoped. On Monday Dr. Jackson said he had done his best for me, but the professors were all opposed to my entrance. Dr. Horner advised me to try the

Filbert Street and Franklin schools. A professor of Jefferson College thought it would be impossible to study there, and advised the New England schools.

During these fruitless efforts my kindly Quaker adviser, whose private lectures I attended, said to me: 'Elizabeth, it is of no use trying. Thee cannot gain admission to these schools. Thee must go to Paris and don masculine attire to gain the necessary knowledge.' Curiously enough, this suggestion of disguise made by good Dr. Warrington was also given me by Doctor Pankhurst, the Professor of Surgery in the largest college in Philadelphia.

Louis Pasteur
Battle with Death

by Dorothy Haas

If the people of little Louis Pasteur's village in France had been asked to guess what he would become when he grew up, few would have said he would become one of the world's greatest scientists. "Little Louis...," they would have said thoughtfully. "Well, have you seen any of the pictures he draws? They are really very good. He will probably grow up to be an artist."

Some of the scientist's boyhood drawings still exist. Artists agree that Louis Pasteur, scientist, could have been—Louis Pasteur, artist!

• • •

"Run for your life!"

"Mad wolf!"

A small boy pushed open the heavy door of his home. He slipped inside, slamming it behind him.

His heart pounding, little Louis Pasteur—for that was

the boy's name—turned. He brushed aside the lace curtain on the window next to the door. The scene outside was something out of a nightmare.

A maddened, snarling wolf, foaming at the mouth, charged down the street. Panic-stricken people scattered before it. Some found shelter. Others, not so lucky, were bitten. Little Louis closed his eyes. He pressed his face into the scratchy lace of the curtain. But he could not shut out those dreadful cries.

Soon the howls of the suffering beast faded in the distance. Then they stopped altogether. The wolf had gone back to the dark forests that surrounded Arbois. Silence returned to the tiny town.

Once more Louis dared to look outside. A pitiful parade was passing by. One by one, the wolf's victims were being helped up the street. They seemed to be going to the blacksmith's shop.

Louis pulled open the door and followed them. What he saw there was to haunt him for the rest of his life.

The only known treatment for rabies, caused by the bite of a mad animal, was a fearful one. Each of the wolf's victims—eight in all—was brought into the blacksmith's shop. There the doctor touched a red-hot poker to the wounds. He was trying to burn away the poisons left there by the sick wolf.

But the treatment was useless. In the weeks that followed, the wolf's victims sickened. At last, one by one, they died. There was no cure for rabies.

Many years passed. The little boy of Arbois grew up. He studied chemistry and biology. He became a scientist, an honored scientist known throughout France. In his laboratory he found the answers to many grave problems.

The farmers' sheep and cattle died in great numbers from a certain disease called anthrax. Dr. Louis Pasteur found a way to vaccinate them, and so to keep them healthy.

Many people became ill and died from drinking the milk of sick cows. Dr. Pasteur developed a method of making milk safe. We still use that method today. It is called pasteurization.

Many were the problems that Dr. Pasteur solved. But during the years he could not forget the cries of the terrified townsfolk of Arbois. The trouble was that no one knew quite where to start on the fearful problem of rabies. For nobody knew what caused the disease. Today we know that it is caused by a virus, a germ so small that it cannot be seen under the usual kind of microscope. But Dr. Pasteur did not know this.

One day he was in his laboratory with his assistant. They were talking about rabies, as they often did. The

elderly scientist, limping from an illness which had left him painfully crippled, moved up and down the long room as they talked.

"We do not know what causes rabies," he said. He paused for a thoughtful moment, leaning on his cane. "But every problem has an answer," he went on. "And to every answer there is a clue. Let's start looking for a clue. We will begin with the sick animals themselves!"

In the weeks that followed, strange guests came to live in Dr. Pasteur's laboratory in Paris: mad rabbits, mad guinea pigs, mad dogs. The scientist studied the disease in these animals. He even studied the **saliva**, which he took from their foaming mouths. But he did not find his clue.

saliva watery fluid in the mouth that moistens chewed food, beginning digestion

He worked long hours. He was in the laboratory, bent over his microscope, long before his assistant opened the door in the morning. And he stayed on, lost in thought, long after his assistant went home at night.

Months went by. Many times Dr. Pasteur thought he had the answer, only to meet with failure. But he did not give up. And then, at last, the long hours of work had their reward.

He injected nerve tissues from sick animals into healthy ones in a certain way. He found that in doing this he could cause rabies in healthy animals. This was because the germs were **concentrated** in the nerve tissue. And this turned out to be the clue that Dr. Pasteur had been waiting for.

He found that by letting this tissue stand for a few days it became weak. When a dog received this weak nerve tissue it became sick, yes. But not so sick that it died. The dog got well. And after that, even if injected with the strongest nerve tissue, the dog did not develop rabies. Its body had built up strength against the disease. The dog was **immune**.

The scientist knew that persons bitten by rabid dogs do not show signs of illness until nearly a month later. If resistance could be built up in these people before they showed signs of the disease, perhaps they might not sicken at all! He worked up a course of treatment. It would take fourteen days.

On the first day a dose of a very weak fourteen-day-old nerve tissue was to be given to a person who had been bitten. This was followed on the second day by a thirteen-day-old dose. And so on, until on the last day strong virus was to be given. During this time the person's body would be building up resistance. Finally, the victim would have so much resistance that he would not get sick.

Dr. Pasteur had found his cure for rabies—or he thought he had. It had been successful with dogs. Would it work

....

concentrated most abundant
immune resistant to or able to fight off disease

as well on a human being? Perhaps it would harm, rather than help, a person who had been bitten!

At last he decided what he would do. He would try the treatment on himself! If he was not harmed by it, then he would be sure that it was safe for everyone.

But something happened before he had a chance to test his cure. It happened on July 6, 1885. Footsteps sounded on the stairway leading to the laboratory. The door was flung open. A woman rushed into the room.

"Dr. Pasteur!" she cried, when she spied the scientist. "I am Madame Meister. I have heard you are working on a cure for rabies. You must help my boy Joseph or he will surely die. We have come all the way from Alsace!"

She turned and pointed to a little boy. He stood in the doorway, smiling shyly at the great scientist. Joseph Meister was nine years old. He had been bitten fourteen times.

Dr. Pasteur stood up, shaking his head. "But, my good woman!" he said. "The treatment has never been tried on a person. It may harm—"

"Please, Doctor!" the woman pleaded. "You are our only hope!"

The scientist was thoughtful. "Let me think," he said. "I will let you know later today."

After Madame Meister and Joseph had gone, the scientist sat down at his desk. Should he use his treatment? Would he be risking great harm to a human life? Perhaps

Laboratory equipment used by Louis Pasteur

Joseph could live, in spite of his wounds....

He talked to his friends, Dr. Grancher and Dr. Vulpian. These two men knew of his work. They went with him to examine Joseph.

When they finished, they turned to their friend. "The boy will surely die," they said. "But if you try your treatment he at least stands a chance of living. By all means, try it!"

Treatment began that very day. In the days that followed, Dr. Pasteur and Joseph became good friends. The scientist watched his little friend worriedly. What if the treatment did not help....

At last the day came when Joseph received the last and strongest dose of the nerve tissue. Dr. Pasteur waited. That night the light in his laboratory burned on long after all the other houses on the street grew dark and silent.

Morning came. The sun rose. The city came alive with the sounds of horses and heavy wagons in the street below. Suddenly there was the sound of flying feet on the stairway. Once more the laboratory door burst open and Madame Meister stood there.

"Dr. Pasteur!" she cried. "Come!" She was gone.

Louis Pasteur limped hurriedly after her. At last he reached Joseph's room. He stopped, his hand on the doorknob. What would he find inside? Would his little friend be well, or would he…. He pushed open the door.

There, sitting up in the big bed, was a smiling boy. A pale—but healthy—Joseph! Beside him stood his mother, tears in her eyes and a smile on her lips.

Joseph gave a little bound, setting the old wooden bed to creaking. "Good morning, Doctor!" he said to his friend.

The scientist could not answer at once. He closed his eyes and took a deep breath. Thank God! His little friend was alive and well!

At last, once and for all, Louis Pasteur was able to erase from his mind the cries of the people of Arbois.

Underwater Adventures

Choose a Sunscreen
Right for Reefs

It's summer, and the sun is hot. You want to spend the day at the beach. But you're worried about getting a sunburn. You know how much a sunburn hurts. You also know that it's dangerous to your health. After all, people with sun-damaged skin are more likely to get skin cancer, a serious disease. So you decide to be smart. You put on plenty of sunscreen to protect your skin. Then you hit the water. But could the sunscreen you wear to keep yourself safe actually harm the planet? If the product contains certain chemicals, the answer is yes. That's why it is very important to choose your sunscreen wisely and only wear sunscreen that is "reef-safe."

Why should you choose to wear reef-safe sunscreen? First, because reef-safe sunscreen does not contain two chemicals: **oxybenzone** and **octinoxate**. In many

---

oxybenzone a common chemical filter used in sunscreen; while its purpose is to absorb UV light, it is also absorbed by the body and is known to be toxic to coral reefs

octinoxate a common ingredient in sunscreens; it is used as a UV light absorber, but it is also absorbed by the body and is known to be toxic to coral reefs

sunscreens, these chemicals help to filter out or block the sun's harmful ultraviolet (UV) rays. However, when they wash off in the ocean, they can be carried by the water to nearby coral reefs. Once there, these chemicals can damage the **coral polyps**. They can make it so the polyps cannot reproduce. They can also kill the algae on the reef. That then triggers a chain reaction. The polyps die, and animals such as parrot fish, which feed on the polyps, have nothing to eat. So they die, as well. Then those fish that eat parrot fish are robbed of their food, too. And once the food chain is broken in this way, it can spell disaster for the reef as a whole.

So how can you make sure that a sunscreen is reef-safe? The easiest way is the check its bottle or tube. Many brands now state, right on the front of the package, that they are reef-safe. Additionally, sunscreens that do contain oxybenzone and octinoxate must list them as ingredients. So it's easy to look on the back of the container for the names of those chemicals. It is not hard to find reef-safe sunscreen, either. It's not as if there are only one or two brands that are reef-safe. Nor are they overly pricey. More than a dozen different reef-safe sunscreens are available in stores and online. Some cost as little as $5 or $10; others cost more than $30 or $40.

....

coral polyps the tiny soft-bodied sea animals responsible for the building of coral reefs

But are reef-safe sunscreens effective? Will they actually protect your skin from sunburn? The simple answer is yes. Reef-safe sunscreens work as well as or better than other sunscreens. That's because rather than using chemicals to block the sun's UV rays, they use physical blockers, such as **zinc oxide**. Zinc oxide is a natural compound. It prevents the harmful UV rays from ever reaching your skin. Instead, zinc oxide reflects sunlight like a mirror. Zinc oxide does not wash off as easily in the ocean, and it does not pose a threat to coral reefs the way chemical blockers do.

Coral reefs are vital to the earth's overall health. They are home to a vast variety of sea life. Plants and animals ranging from the simplest kinds of algae to some of the earth's most unusual and amazing fish live in and around coral

zinc oxide oxide of zinc, which is a white powder used as a pigment, in cosmetics, in glass, in inks, and in zinc ointment

reefs. Reefs are really beautiful, too, and they can even protect people from dangerous waves headed to shore. So it's important to protect them. Buying reef-safe sunscreen is an easy, inexpensive way to do the right thing. So think about that the next time you're headed to the beach, and be sure to take good care of both your body and your planet.

Sources

"The South Florida Reef Ambassador Initiative – Become a Coral Champion!" *Florida Department of Environmental Protection,* 28 Aug. 2018, floridadep.gov/fco/coral/content/south-florida-reef-ambassador-initiative-become-coral-champion.

"Zinc Oxide." *ChemicalSafetyFacts.org,* 13 June 2018, www.chemicalsafetyfacts.org/zinc-oxide/.

Rattini, Kristin Baird. *Coral Reefs.* National Geographic, 2015.

Chin, Jason. *Coral Reefs.* A Neal Porter Book/Roaring Brook Press, 2016.

Life Choices

Tayo's Wishes

It was noon. The sun was high. Crates of yams stood along the edge of the field. And the dull ache in Tayo Okafor's back was now a burning pain, just as it always was after a hard day's work.

For Tayo, every day of harvest season was the same. He was in the field before dawn. For hours, he drove his spade deep into the dirt over and over. He pulled the yams out of the ground, knocked some of the soil off them, and stacked them in a nearby crate. Finally, at midday, when Tayo's back felt like it was about to break, he collected the yams and went home.

Everyone in Tayo's village knew how hard he worked. When they saw him, they'd call out, "There goes Tayo Okafor, the hardest working man in all of Nigeria."

Hearing their words made Tayo proud, but it didn't make the work easier. It didn't relieve his aching back. That day, his back was even more painful than usual, so Tayo took a shortcut home. He walked across the Hills of Belesa.

It was a fateful decision.

The Hills of Belesa were not just another set of charming **hummocks**, covered in the green bushes and massive palm trees of the Nigerian countryside, that were described as "magical" or "enchanted" simply because they were beautiful. No, the Hills of Belesa were special. They actually were magical. They truly were enchanted.

Yes, the Hills of Belesa were popular with many minor gods and goddesses. They were where these gods and goddesses came to play and relax. Which is why, that day, Tayo saw a god named Eshu there.

....

hummocks small round hills

"My goodness!" Tayo exclaimed upon spotting Eshu, who was a foot shorter than Tayo and wore a helmet made of pure gold. "What is it you're doing here on the Hills of Belesa?"

Eshu stopped in his tracks. He wasn't supposed to be out at midday. And to be found by a human was against every rule the gods and goddesses had. He thought fast.

"Three wishes!" he said.

"What?" asked Tayo.

"I am Eshu of Orun, and I have decided to grant you... uh...what's your name?"

"Tayo Okafor."

"Decided to grant you, Tayo Okafor, three wishes!"

"Why?" Tayo asked.

"Because you are a...noble...em...what is it you do for a living, Tayo Okafor?"

"I'm a yam farmer—"

"Because you are a noble yam farmer!" Eshu finished. "And because I am a kind god who will be grateful if you don't tell the other gods and goddesses you found me. Which would get me in trouble."

Tayo smiled at his good fortune. He privately patted himself on his aching back for choosing to walk over the Hills of Belesa. Then he said:

"And you will not be tricking me, I hope? Not using these wishes to teach me some lesson about appreciating what I have, yes?"

"I had not thought of that," said Eshu.

"Good," Tayo said. "Because I haven't got a thing in this world."

"Excellent. What is it you wish for, Tayo Okafor, the yam farmer?"

Now, many people would've waited to make their first wish. Some would have asked others for advice about what to wish for. But not Tayo. He made his first wish immediately.

"Every day, I dig and stack yams for hours. I wish, from now on, for the yams to be dug and stacked in crates when I get to the field."

Eshu looked at Tayo. "You're sure?" he asked. "Because I don't want to grant this wish and have you decide it was a mistake and end up listening to you complain and having to undo it."

But Tayo was sure. How nice it would be not to have such hard work to do each day!

"Very well, then, it is granted. What's your second wish?"

"My second wish," Tayo said, "has to do with my back. Every morning, I—

"Your back hurts and you want it to feel better," Eshu interrupted. "Is that it?"

"You are an impatient god," said Tayo.

"You barely took five seconds to start wishing. Who's impatient?" Eshu returned.

"Fair enough," Tayo said. "Yes, my back hurts."

"It is healed," Eshu said.

And it was. Tayo stood up straight and marveled that his pain was gone.

"Third wish, then?" Eshu said.

But now Tayo felt like it was a trap. He wasn't ready to make his final wish. He wanted to see if his work really was finished when he went to the field the next day and make sure his back pain didn't return. So he thanked Eshu and headed to his home.

The next morning, Tayo woke up early. His back felt great.

He went to the field. There, in dozens of crates, sat hundreds of neatly stacked yams.

Tayo smiled. His wishes had come true.

The days and weeks after that passed quickly. Tayo began to sleep later, for he had no real work to do. His back never bothered him, and his days were free and easy. For a long time, it was nice.

But one day, Tayo noticed that he felt a bit bored. He felt no satisfaction just collecting the yams. And he realized that nobody had called him the hardest working man in all of Nigeria for some time. That made him unhappy.

The next day was a bit worse: more boredom, more dissatisfaction, more unhappiness. And so it was the day after that, and the day after that, and the day after that. Until, at last, Tayo couldn't stand it. He returned to the Hills of Belesa and called out for Eshu.

"What is it you're shouting about?" said the god, annoyed at being called out of his hillside retreat.

Tayo told Eshu of his boredom, his dissatisfaction, and his unhappiness. He told of how no one commented on how hard he worked anymore.

"And the worst part," Tayo said, "is that I'm no longer Tayo Okafor, the yam farmer. I'm Tayo Okafor, who has nothing to do all day long."

Eshu shook his head.

"Just as I predicted. Humans *always* do this. 'Be careful what you wish for, because you just might get it.' Ever hear that saying?"

"Yes," said Tayo **sheepishly**, but he looked at Eshu with real hurt in his eyes, and the god took pity on him.

"You have one wish left, you know. Shall we use it as you humans always use it? To undo your previous two wishes and make things just like they were before?"

"No," said Tayo. "I mean, yes, but also no."

"Are you trying to confuse me?" Eshu asked.

"I mean, could I use the third wish to only undo the first wish? The one about having my work all done each day?"

"I don't see why not," Eshu replied. "So keep the second wish, then?"

"Yes," said Tayo. "'It is truly wonderful not to have an aching back anymore."

---

sheepishly in a meek, timid, or bashful manner, like a sheep

Eshu smiled. And he told Tayo that his third wish was granted. Once again, he would have to wake before dawn. Once again, he would have to drive his spade deep into the dirt over and over. Once again, he would have to pull the yams out of the ground, knock some of the soil off them, and stack them in nearby crates. And once again, he would be Tayo Okafor, the yam farmer.

But his back would always feel great.

The Green Glass Ball

an Irish folktale dramatized by Hazel W. Corson

Characters

TINKER, older man who repairs

DONKEY, the tinker's companion

TERRY, a boy who works for Mike

MIKE, a farmer

TIM, the tinker's nephew

TWO WOMEN

TWO MEN

OLD WOMAN

GIRL

BOY'S MOTHER

BOY

Scene 1

Time: Long ago

Setting: A small village in Ireland

At Rise: Tinker and Donkey enter right and walk slowly to center.

TINKER: 'Tis a beautiful day. The sun is shining! The birds are singing!

DONKEY: That's all right for you to say! All you have to do is stroll around without a care in the world while I have to carry a heavy pack.

....

tinker a traveling mender of things

TINKER: Oh, I work, too. And we both have a chance to move about, meeting people and hearing the news. Isn't that better than staying on a farm, plowing the same field and talking to the same three people day after day?

DONKEY: I suppose so. *(Looks around)* Here we come to a village.

TINKER: I can see that you are in a bad mood this morning, Donkey. Cheer up! Things aren't that bad. Who knows what the day will bring? *(Tinker and Donkey stop at center. Tinker shouts in a loud, singsong voice.)* Any rags, any bottles, any bones today? Scissors sharpened! Knives ground! Pots and pans mended! I buy old rags, old bottles, old bones! *(He takes pack off Donkey's back and sets it on the ground. He takes small grindstone and iron kettle out of pack. Terry enters carrying hoe, goes up to Tinker.)*

TERRY: Good morning, tinker.

TINKER: Good morning, lad.

TERRY: Can you use a boy to travel with you and help you, and learn to be a tinker?

TINKER *(Doubtfully)*: Well, I don't know. What is your name, lad?

TERRY: My name is Terry, sir.

TINKER: You are a likely-looking lad, Terry, and could make a good tinker, if you tried.

TERRY: Then you'll take me?

TINKER (Shaking head): No, my lad, I'm sorry. I have a young nephew, Tim, who is lame. There are many things Tim cannot do, but he could be a tinker, and I plan to teach him.

TERRY: But how can Tim walk about the country?

TINKER: I must find a way for him to ride. Someday, in my travels, I'll find someone with a cart to sell or trade. But you must keep trying to learn a trade, Terry. Be your own man. (1st Woman enters, carrying a pot and sack. Terry stands back, and watches Tinker.)

1ST WOMAN: Good morning, tinker. Here is a pot I've been saving for you to mend. (Hands Tinker pot)

TINKER: Good morning to you. (Looks the pot over) There's many a good soup been cooked in that pot, I'll be bound.

1ST WOMAN: Yes. And there'll be many a good soup to come, if you can fix it.

TINKER: It can be fixed, and it will still be a better pot than you can buy today. I've heard there's a new **ironmonger** in the next village who makes good wares, but I've not seen his work.

2ND WOMAN: That would be Jock. He's an honest lad, and will do a good job of work at anything he tries. (Tinker finishes mending pot, looks it over, and gives it to 1st Woman.)

....

ironmonger one who deals in iron or hardware

TINKER: There you are, ma'am. That should serve you for a good long time.

1ST WOMAN: Thank you, tinker. What do I owe you?

TINKER: Fourpence would be about right.

1ST WOMAN: And cheap enough, too. I don't have fourpence, but here is a sack of potatoes. They should be worth fourpence. *(Donkey stamps feet impatiently as Tinker takes sack. 2nd Woman enters, carrying basket.)*

TINKER: Thank you. One can always eat potatoes.

2ND WOMAN *(Stepping forward)*: Here are some knives to sharpen, tinker.

TINKER: I'll gladly sharpen them. *(He takes knives and pretends to sharpen them on his grindstone. As he works, Boy, carrying kettle and sack, and Girl with wooden doll enter right. Two Men enter left. All gather around Tinker.)* A dull knife can be as dangerous as a sharp one, you know. *(Mike rushes in right. Terry ducks down behind others, and exits quickly.)*

MIKE: Has anyone seen that good-for-nothing lad, Terry?

1ST MAN: And where should Terry be, Mike?

MIKE *(Angrily)*: Hoeing beans in my field—that's where he should be!

2ND MAN: Maybe that's where he is.

MIKE: I doubt it!

TINKER: And what is this Terry to you, sir?

MIKE: He is a boy I keep out of the kindness of my heart, because he belongs to no one. And a great worry he is, with his hungry mouth and his shiftless ways.

TINKER: Then why not take him to young Jock, the ironmonger in the next village? He may need a boy.

2ND MAN: Aye. Jock is looking for a likely boy.

MIKE: I may do that. The boy will never make a farmer! *(Stomps off)*

TINKER *(To 2nd Woman)*: Now, here are your knives, ma'am. Be careful. Very sharp they are. *(Hands them to 2nd Woman)*

2ND WOMAN: Thank you, tinker. How much do I owe you?

TINKER: Sixpence, all told.

2ND WOMAN: I have no money, but here are some cabbages that should be worth sixpence. *(Hands him cabbages from basket)*

TINKER: Thank you ma'am. *(Donkey stamps.)*

BOY: My mother wants to know if you can mend her kettle. All she has to pay is this bag of apples. *(Tinker takes kettle and examines it.)*

TINKER: I guess I can do it. It isn't a very big hole. *(Starts to work on kettle)*

1ST MAN: How is haying around the country coming on, tinker?

TINKER: It looks like a good crop this year, but with all the rain, hard to dry. It doesn't do to put green hay in a barn, or even in a haycock. The hay heats up and may catch on fire. Why, only last week such a thing happened to Jim Kelly. His barn was filled with green hay and it caused a fire.

2ND MAN: What a terrible thing!

TINKER *(Handing kettle to Boy)*: Here you are, my lad.

BOY: Thank you, tinker. *(Takes kettle, but stays to watch)*

GIRL: My doll has a broken leg, tinker. Can you fix her?

(Tinker looks at doll, hunts through his pockets.)

TINKER: Well, that's not bad. *(He works on doll.)* I'll make a little hole here, and one here. Now a bit of wire to fasten it together, and here she is. She can bend her knee now. *(Hands doll back)*

GIRL: Oh, thank you, tinker. Here is a pretty pebble for you. It is my good luck pebble.

TINKER *(Taking pebble)*: Thank you. It is a very pretty pebble. *(Donkey stamps.)*

BOY'S MOTHER *(Rushing in)*: So here you are! I've been waiting for that kettle! *(Takes Boy by ear and leads him offstage. Tinker starts to pack up his things.)*

1ST MAN: I'd better go, or my wife will be after me by the ear. *(As he exits)* Come again soon, tinker. You always bring us news.

2ND MAN: 'Twas a good thing you did for young Terry. I'll put in a good word with Jock for the boy myself. Now I must be off, too. Goodbye, tinker. *(He exits followed by Girl and Women.)*

TINKER *(Waving)*: Goodbye. *(Old Woman hobbles on, carrying kettle.)*

OLD WOMAN *(In a quavering voice)*: Can you fix my kettle, tinker?

TINKER *(Examining kettle)*: Now, that is as old as I have ever seen, but still, a good kettle. Yes, I can fix it.

OLD WOMAN: Many a year has that kettle hung in the fireplace, and strange stories it could tell. *(Tinker works on kettle and soon finishes.)*

TINKER: Here is your kettle, Mother.

OLD WOMAN: Bless you, tinker. It has been many a year since anyone called me "Mother." "Old Hag Blakewell," but never "Mother."

TINKER: The more shame to them for their bad manners, Mother.

OLD WOMAN *(Taking kettle and looking it over)*: Now that is a fine job of mending. I can see that you are no ordinary tinker.

TINKER: Thank you. That will be fourpence.

OLD WOMAN: I have no money to pay you, tinker, but you have been so kind to a poor old woman that I will give you a special gift. *(She takes a green glass ball from her pocket and hands it to Tinker. Donkey stomps and sniffs loudly.)*

TINKER *(Holding up ball):* This is very pretty, Mother, but neither my donkey nor I can eat it.

OLD WOMAN: Ah, but this is a magic ball, and better than food.

TINKER *(Sighing)*: I know of nothing better than food.

OLD WOMAN: Hold this magic ball in your hand and make a wish—and one wish only—for the thing you want most in the world, and that wish will come true.

TINKER: Oh, I don't believe it.

OLD WOMAN: It is true. The fairies made this ball many years ago and gave it to a mortal. Since then, it has passed from person to person, each one making one wish. I was the last to have it, and now it will be yours.

TINKER: Why didn't you wish for gold when you had the chance, Mother? Then you could be paying me now.

OLD WOMAN: Alas, I wished my one wish when I was young, and it was not a kind or a generous wish and little good it did me. Think well before you wish and perhaps you will fare better than I. And remember, wishes can be dangerous. No good comes from them, unless you make the wish for someone else. *(She exits.)*

TINKER *(Watching her exit)*: Well, Donkey, now we have a green glass ball, and one wish.

DONKEY *(Crossly)*: And much good may it do us. *(Curtain)*

Scene 2

Time: A short while later

Setting: A country road. Scene is played before curtain.

At Rise: Tinker and Donkey enter right and walk to center.

TINKER: It's been a good day, Donkey. Jock the ironmonger will take young Terry, we will be getting home early, and a fine lot of business we did today!

DONKEY: If you call it business—listening to a lot of chatterboxes.

TINKER: Everyone brought me something to mend and sharpen.

DONKEY: Yes, and not so much as one tuppence in the lot of them.

TINKER: They all gave me something—potatoes, apples, cabbages—

DONKEY (*In disgust*): And the green glass ball! That was the most useless thing of all!

TINKER: I'm not sure of that.

DONKEY: Well, I am. Pray, what am I to eat tonight?

TINKER: There is plenty of grass to eat, and I know you always like a fine red apple.

DONKEY: You should have kept the old woman's kettle, and exchanged it for oats for me.

TINKER: Donkey, you have been complaining all day. Look— here comes Tim to meet us. Be done with your complaints. (*Tim enters. He pats Donkey on head and smiles at Tinker.*)

TIM: Donkey, I suppose you and Uncle have been quarreling. What is it this time?

DONKEY: The usual thing. I can't teach him anything. He works for nothing. Today, we did not even take in one coin.

TINKER: But we did a good day's work, and we are better off than we were this morning. Besides, we have a magic ball.

TIM: A magic ball?

TINKER: See how beautiful it is, and how the light shines through it. *(Holds up ball)*

DONKEY: Humph! You said yourself that we can't eat it.

TINKER: True enough! But something beautiful is worth any price.

THE GREEN GLASS BALL

TIM: How did you get it?

TINKER: An old woman gave it to me for mending her kettle. She said I must hold it in my hand and make a wish—only one wish—for the thing I want most in the world, and it will come true.

TIM: Are you going to try it?

TINKER: Indeed, I am! I have been waiting for you to help me! Now what shall I wish for?

TIM: Don't you think you should put the ball down until you are ready to wish, Uncle? It would be too bad to wish by accident.

TINKER: True enough. *(Donkey sits in front of curtain opening. Tinker places the ball in front of him.)*

TIM: What do you want the most?

DONKEY: Why don't you wish for a lot of money? Then you could buy me oats every day.

TINKER: Money isn't everything. Why don't I wish for a fine cart?

DONKEY: So I can pull it around the country, I suppose. No, thank you.

TINKER: If you are so smart, what would you have me wish for?

DONKEY: Why don't you wish to be a king? Then I could be the king's donkey. I could have a fine stable to live in, and grooms to care for me. What a life!

TINKER: What a life indeed! A king has many worries. He may live in a fine palace, with many servants, and fine food, but a king can never be sure who his friends are. That is a stupid wish, Donkey. *(Tinker picks up the ball and watches the light shine on it.)*

DONKEY *(Angrily)*: So now you say I am stupid! I don't know what you would do without me to help you. If it were not for me, you would starve! Stupid, indeed!

TINKER *(Angrily to Donkey)*: I have listened to your scolding all this day. I wish you were at the ends of the earth! *(There is a crash, then a bang. Donkey disappears through opening of curtain.)*

TIM: Oh, Uncle! What have you done?

TINKER: I didn't mean it! I forgot that the ball was in my hands. How could I know that the wish would really come true? 'Twas only a little old woman who said so! What can I do?

TIM *(Slowly)*: Do you think I could have a wish?

TINKER: I don't know why not.

TIM: Then I will wish for donkey to be back.

TINKER: Oh, Tim! 'Twould please me greatly to have the donkey back, cross as he is, sometimes. But what about you? Would you not like to be cured of your lameness?

TIM: I would rather have the donkey back, and see you happy again, Uncle. Let me give my wish to you and the donkey. *(Tinker gives ball to Tim, who places it carefully on the ground.)*

TINKER: Wish carefully then, Tim. *(Puts ball into Tim's hands, and leans forward, anxiously)*

TIM *(Slowly)*: I wish the tinker's little donkey back, alive and well! (There is a crash, then a bang, and Donkey bursts through the curtains.)

DONKEY *(Angrily)*: What a trick to play on your faithful donkey! How could you be so thoughtless! Now you have wasted your wish!

TIM: But, donkey, we used my wish to bring you back. If you are going to be so bad-tempered, we shall be sorry that we didn't leave you at the ends of the earth. *(Donkey hangs his head.)*

TINKER: Oh, my poor little Donkey! How glad I am to have you back! Are you all right?

DONKEY *(Thoughtfully)*: Yes, I guess I'm all right. It's too bad we lost the wishes. It was my fault. I complained too much.

TINKER: It was my fault. I lost my temper. *(Tinker hugs Donkey.)*

TIM: What are you going to do with the ball now, Uncle?

TINKER: It isn't any good to us anymore, and somehow it doesn't seem beautiful to me now. I'll toss it away. *(Starts to throw ball away)*

TIM: Wait, Uncle! Suppose someone finds it and makes a terrible wish!

DONKEY: Or a careless wish, not knowing it would come true?

TINKER: I didn't think of that. This magic ball could cause a lot of trouble. I'll smash it.

TIM: But what if each piece is magic? There might be millions of terrible wishes made.

DONKEY: That would be worse than ever! What can we do with it? *(They all think.)*

OLD WOMAN *(Calling from behind curtain)*: Tinker! Tinker! (Old Woman enters.) Oh, tinker! Such a time as I've had! Are you all right?

TINKER: Yes, I'm all right. But how did you find me? How did you get here?

OLD WOMAN: Never mind that. I've come to stop you from making a bad wish. I've been worried ever since I gave you that ball.

TINKER *(Sadly)*: It's too late, Mother. I wished foolishly. If I had only wished for the cart, Tim could go with us when we travel.

OLD WOMAN: But no one was hurt by your foolish wish?

TINKER: No. Tim made a wish that fixed everything.

OLD WOMAN: What's done is done! Give me the ball. *(Tinker hands ball to Old Woman.)*

TINKER: And what will you do with it?

OLD WOMAN: It is a dangerous thing. I know a place, far from here, where there is a deep bog, filled with quicksand. I will drop the ball in the middle of that quicksand.

DONKEY: When you drop the ball into the quicksand, it will drop out of sight forever.

OLD WOMAN: Yes, but it will not soon be forgotten. This green glass ball has taught us a good lesson: Never make a mean wish. When you wish for something, make it a kind wish, a generous wish. *(She exits as curtain falls.)*

The Gold Coin

by Alma Flor Ada

Juan had been a thief for many years. Because he did his stealing by night, his skin had become pale and sickly. Because he spent his time either hiding or sneaking about, his body had become shriveled and bent. And because he had neither friend nor relative to make him smile, his face was always twisted into an angry frown.

One night, drawn by a light shining through the trees, Juan came upon a hut. He crept up to the door, and through a crack saw an old woman sitting at a plain wooden table.

What was that shining in her hand? Juan wondered. He could not believe his eyes: It was a gold coin. Then he heard the woman say to herself, "I must be the richest person in the world."

Juan decided instantly that all the woman's gold must be his. He thought that the easiest thing to do was to watch until the woman left. Juan hid in the bushes and

huddled under his **poncho**, waiting for the right moment to enter the hut.

Juan was half asleep when he heard knocking at the door and the sound of insistent voices. A few minutes later, he saw the woman, wrapped in a black **cloak**, leave the hut with two men at her side.

Here's my chance! Juan thought. And, forcing open a window, he climbed into the empty hut.

....

poncho a blanket worn as a garment, with a hole in the middle for the head
cloak a loose outer garment

He looked about eagerly for the gold. He looked under the bed. It wasn't there. He looked in the cupboard. It wasn't there, either. Where could it be? Close to despair, Juan tore away some beams supporting the thatch roof.

Finally, he gave up. There was simply no gold in the hut.

All I can do, he thought, is to find the old woman and make her tell me where she's hidden it.

So he set out along the path that she and her two companions had taken.

It was daylight by the time Juan reached the river. The countryside had been deserted, but here, along the riverbank, were two huts. Nearby, a man and his son were hard at work, hoeing potatoes.

It had been a long, long time since Juan had spoken to another human being. Yet his desire to find the woman was so strong that he went up to the farmers and asked, in a hoarse, raspy voice, "Have you seen a short, gray-haired woman, wearing a black cloak?"

"Oh, you must be looking for Doña Josefa," the young boy said. "Yes, we've seen her. We went to fetch her this morning, because my grandfather had another attack of—"

"Where is she now?" Juan broke in.

"She is long gone," said the father with a smile. "Some people from across the river came looking for her, because someone in their family is sick."

"How can I get across the river?" Juan asked anxiously.

"Only by boat," the boy answered. "We'll row you across later, if you'd like." Then turning back to his work, he added, "But first we must finish digging up the potatoes."

The thief muttered, "Thanks." But he quickly grew impatient. He grabbed a hoe and began to help the pair of farmers. The sooner we finish, the sooner we'll get across the river, he thought. And the sooner I'll get to my gold!

It was dusk when they finally laid down their hoes. The soil had been turned, and the wicker baskets were brimming with potatoes.

"Now can you row me across?" Juan asked the father anxiously.

"Certainly," the man said. "But let's eat supper first."

Juan had forgotten the taste of a home-cooked meal and the pleasure that comes from sharing it with others. As he sopped up the last of the stew with a chunk of dark bread, memories of other meals came back to him from far away and long ago.

By the light of the moon, father and son guided their boat across the river.

"What a wonderful healer Doña Josefa is!" the boy told Juan.

"All she had to do to make Abuelo better was give him a cup of her special tea."

"Yes, and not only that," his father added, "she brought him a gold coin."

Juan was stunned. It was one thing for Doña Josefa to go around helping people. But how could she go around handing out gold coins—his gold coins?

When the threesome finally reached the other side of the river, they saw a young man sitting outside his hut.

"This fellow is looking for Doña Josefa," the father said, pointing to Juan.

"Oh, she left some time ago," the young man said.

"Where to?" Juan asked tensely.

"Over to the other side of the mountain," the young man replied, pointing to the vague outline of mountains in the night sky.

"How did she get there?" Juan asked, trying to hide his impatience.

"By horse," the young man answered. "They came on horseback to get her because someone had broken his leg."

"Well, then, I need a horse, too," Juan said urgently.

"Tomorrow," the young man replied softly. "Perhaps I can take you tomorrow, maybe the next day. First I must finish harvesting the corn."

So Juan spent the next day in the fields, bathed in sweat from sunup to sundown.

Yet each ear of corn that he picked seemed to bring him

closer to his treasure. And later that evening, when he helped the young man husk several ears so they could boil them for supper, the yellow kernels glittered like gold coins.

While they were eating, Juan thought about Doña Josefa. Why, he wondered, would someone who said she was the world's richest woman spend her time taking care of every sick person for miles around?

The following day, the two set off at dawn. Juan could not recall when he last had noticed the beauty of the sunrise. He felt strangely moved by the sight of the mountains, barely lit by the faint rays of the morning sun.

As they neared the foothills, the young man said, "I'm not surprised you're looking for Doña Josefa. The whole countryside needs her. I went for her because my wife had been running a high fever. In no time at all, Doña Josefa had her on the road to recovery. And what's more, my friend, she brought her a gold coin!"

Juan groaned inwardly. To think that someone could hand out gold so freely! What a strange woman Doña Josefa is, Juan thought. Not only is she willing to help one person after another, but she doesn't mind traveling all over the countryside to do it!

"Well, my friend," said the young man finally, "this is where I must leave you. But you don't have far to walk. See that house over there? It belongs to the man who broke his leg."

The young man stretched out his hand to say goodbye. Juan stared at it for a moment. It had been a long, long time since the thief had shaken hands with anyone. Slowly, he pulled out a hand from under his poncho. When his companion grasped it firmly in his own, Juan felt suddenly warmed, as if by the rays of the sun.

But after he thanked the young man, Juan ran down the road. He was still eager to catch up with Doña Josefa. When he reached the house, a woman and a child were stepping down from a wagon.

"Have you seen Doña Josefa?" Juan asked.

"We've just taken her to Don Teodosio," the woman said. "His wife is sick, you know—"

"How do I get there?" Juan broke in. "I've got to see her."

"It's too far to walk," the woman said amiably. "If you'd like, I'll take you there tomorrow. But first I must gather my squash and beans."

So Juan spent yet another long day in the fields. Working beneath the summer sun, Juan noticed that his skin had begun to tan. And although he had to stoop down to pick the squash, he found that he could now stretch his body. His back had begun to straighten, too.

Later, when the little girl took him by the hand to show him a family of rabbits burrowed under a fallen tree, Juan's face broke into a smile. It had been a long, long time since Juan had smiled.

Yet his thoughts kept coming back to the gold.

The following day, the wagon carrying Juan and the woman **lumbered** along a road lined with coffee fields.

The woman said, "I don't know what we would have done without Doña Josefa. I sent my daughter to our neighbor's house, who then brought Doña Josefa on horseback. She set my husband's leg and then showed me how to brew a special tea to lessen the pain."

Getting no reply she went on. "And, as if that weren't enough, she brought him a gold coin. Can you imagine such a thing?"

Juan could only sigh. No doubt about it, he thought, Doña Josefa is someone special. But Juan didn't know whether to be happy that Doña Josefa had so much gold she could freely hand it out, or angry for her having already given so much of it away.

When they finally reached Don Teodosio's house, Doña Josefa was already gone. But here, too, there was work that needed to be done....

Juan stayed to help with the coffee harvest. As he picked the red berries, he gazed up from time to time at the trees that grew, row upon row, along the hillsides. What a calm, peaceful place this is! he thought.

....

lumbered moved along heavily or awkwardly

The next morning, Juan was up at daybreak. Bathed in the soft, dawn light, the mountains seemed to smile at him. When Don Teodosio offered him a lift on horseback, Juan found it difficult to have to say good-bye.

"What a good woman Doña Josefa is!" Don Teodosio said, as they rode down the hill toward the sugarcane fields. "The minute she heard about my wife being sick, she came with her special herbs. And as if that weren't enough, she brought my wife a gold coin!"

In the stifling heat, the kind that often signals the approach of a storm, Juan simply sighed and mopped his brow. The pair continued riding for several hours in silence.

Juan then realized he was back in familiar territory, for they were now on the stretch of road he had traveled only a week ago—though how much longer it now seemed to him. He jumped off Don Teodosio's horse and broke into a run.

This time the gold would not escape him! But he had to move quickly, so he could find shelter before the storm broke.

Out of breath, Juan finally reached Doña Josefa's hut. She was standing by the door, shaking her head slowly as she surveyed the **ransacked** house.

"So I've caught up with you at last!" Juan shouted, startling the old woman. "Where's the gold?"

....

ransacked destructively searched

"The gold coin?" Doña Josefa said, surprised and looking at Juan intently. "Have you come for the gold coin? I've been trying hard to give it to someone who might need it," Doña Josefa said. "First to an old man who had just gotten over a bad attack. Then to a man with a broken leg. And finally to Don Teodosio's wife. But none of them would take it. They all said, 'Keep it. There must be someone who needs it more.'"

Juan did not say a word.

"You must be the one who needs it," Doña Josefa said.

She took the coin out of her pocket and handed it to him. Juan stared at the coin, speechless.

At that moment a young girl appeared, her long braid bouncing as she ran. "Hurry, Doña Josefa, please!" she said breathlessly. "My mother is all alone, and the baby is due any minute."

"Of course, dear," Doña Josefa replied. But as she glanced up at the sky, she saw nothing but black clouds. The storm was nearly upon them. Doña Josefa sighed deeply.

"But how can I leave now? Look at my house! I don't know what has happened to the roof. The storm will wash the whole place away!"

And there was a deep sadness in her voice.

Juan took in the child's frightened eyes, Doña Josefa's sad, distressed face, and the ransacked hut.

"Go ahead, Doña Josefa," he said. "Don't worry about your house. I'll see that the roof is back in shape, good as new."

The woman nodded gratefully, drew her cloak about her shoulders, and took the child by the hand. As she turned to leave, Juan held out his hand.

"Here, take this," he said, giving her the gold coin. "I'm sure the newborn will need it more than I."

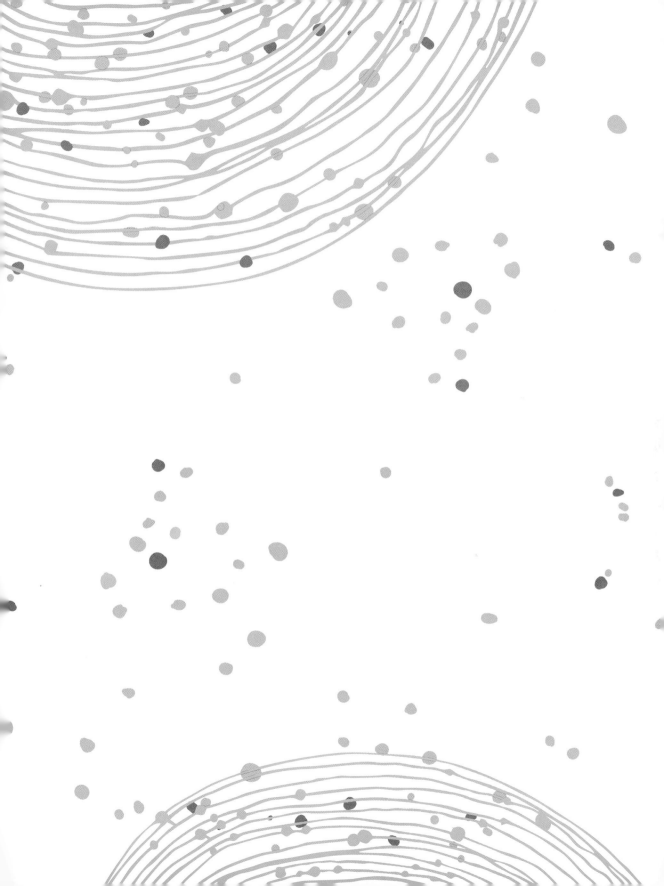

The Grateful Stork

a Japanese folktale retold by Yoshiko Uchida

Once long ago, there lived a kind old man and woman who were very, very poor. Each day the old man went out to cut wood in the forest nearby, and then took bundles of kindling into town to sell. The old man went out even when snow fell or great icicles dangled from the roof, for if he didn't sell any wood, there would be no money for their food.

One cold, snowy day, the old man set out for the village as usual, with a bundle of kindling strapped to his back. Great soft snowflakes were swirling down from the gray sky, making shapeless white heaps everywhere.

"Ah, how nice it would be to be back home," the old man thought with a sigh. But he knew he could not turn back, and he trudged on down the snow-covered road, beating his hands to keep them warm.

Suddenly, he saw something strange in the middle of a field. Great white wings seemed to be fluttering and churning up a flurry of snow.

"What is this?" the old man thought, rubbing his eyes. "It looks like a little snowstorm in the middle of the field."

The old man moved closer, and saw that it was a beautiful white stork that had been caught in a trap. The bird fluttered wildly as it tried to get away, but the more it struggled, the tighter the rope around its leg became.

"Poor frightened bird," said the old man, and even though he was shivering from the cold and anxious to get to town, he stopped to help the stork.

"Here, here," he called gently. "Wait a minute. You're getting all tangled in the rope." And bending down, he loosened the rope around the stork's leg. "Let me untie you quickly, before someone comes along and wants to take you home."

When the rope was undone, the stork beat its great white wings and flew off into the sky. The old man heard it crying into the wind as it soared higher and higher. Then, it circled over the old man's head three times, and flew off toward the mountains.

"Good-bye, stork! Good luck!" the old man called, and he watched until it became a small black speck in the sky. Then, picking up his kindling, he hurried toward the village. It was bitterly cold, but inside the old man felt a warm happy glow. Somehow, the stork seemed to be a good omen, and he felt glad to have helped it get away.

He sold all his kindling in the village and then hurried home to tell the old woman how he had saved a stork that had been caught in a trap.

"You did a good thing, my husband," the old woman said, and the two old people thought of the stork flying home into the hills.

Outside, the snow still fell, piling up all along the sides of the house. "How good it is to be inside on a night like this," the old man said, as he heard the rice sputtering in the kitchen and smelled the good bean soup that bubbled in a pot beside it.

Just then, there was a soft rap-rap-rap at the door.

"Now who could be out on a cold night like this?" the old man thought. But before he could get to the door, he heard a gentle voice calling, *"Gomen kudasai...* Is anybody home?"

The old woman hurried to the door. "Who is it?" she called, as she slid open the wooden door. There she saw a white figure covered with snow.

"Come in, come in," the old woman urged. "You must be terribly cold."

"Thank you, yes. It is bitterly cold outside," the stranger said, and she came in shaking the snow from her shoulders. Then the old man and woman saw that she was a beautiful young girl of about seventeen. Her cheeks and her hands were red from the cold.

"Dear child, where are you going on such a terrible night?" they asked.

"I was going to visit some friends in the next village," the young girl explained. "But it is growing dark and I can no longer follow the road. Will you be good enough to let me sleep here just for tonight?"

"I wish we could help you," the old woman said sadly. "But, alas, we are very poor, and we have no quilts to offer you."

"Oh, but I am young," the girl answered. "I don't need any quilts."

"And we can offer you no more than a bowl of rice and soup for supper," the old man added.

But the young girl just shook her head and laughed. "I shall be happy to eat anything you are going to have," she said. "Please do not worry."

So the old man and woman welcomed the young girl into their home, saying, "Come in, come in. Get warm beside the **hibachi**."

But the young girl went instead to the kitchen where the old woman was preparing supper. "Let me help you," she said and she worked carefully and quickly. When they had eaten, she got up and washed the dishes before the old woman could tell her to stop.

"You are indeed a good and kind child," the old man and woman said happily, and because they had no children, they wished they could keep her as their own child.

The next morning, the young girl awoke early, and when the old man and woman got up, they found the house swept and the rice bubbling over the charcoal. It was the first time the old woman had had breakfast made for her. "My, you are such a help to me!" she said over and over again.

After breakfast, they looked outside, but snow was still swirling down and had piled so high around the house, they couldn't even open the door.

"Will you let me stay another day?" the young girl asked.

---

hibachi a small charcoal grill

The old man and woman nodded quickly. "Why, of course," they said. "Stay as long as you like. Since you have come, our house seems to be filled with the sunshine of spring."

Each morning, the three of them looked outside, but the roads were still filled with snow, and the young girl could not venture out. Before long, five days had gone by, and still she could not leave. Finally, on the morning of the sixth day, she came before the old man and woman and said, "I have something I would like to ask you."

"Anything, anything," they answered. "We will do anything you ask us to do, for we have come to love you as our own daughter."

Then, bending her head low, the young girl began to speak. "You see, my mother and father have just died. I was on my way to the next village to live with some relatives whom I do not even know. I would so much rather stay here with you. If you will let me be your daughter, I will work hard and be a good and faithful child."

When the old man and woman heard this, they could scarcely believe their good fortune, for they had prayed all these years for a child to comfort them in their old age. The good gods had surely heard their prayer to send them such a sweet and gentle child.

"You have made us happier than we can say," they answered to the young girl. "From this day on, we will love you and care for you as if you were our very own."

And so it was decided that the young girl would stay with them always.

One day, the young girl set up a small wooden loom in the corner of the room, and put a screen around it so no one could look in.

"I would like to weave something," she said to the old man. "Will you buy me some thread the next time you go to the village?"

So the old man bought all sorts of beautiful colored thread and gave it to the young girl.

"Now," she said, "I am going to weave something behind that screen, but no matter what happens, you must not look in while I am weaving."

The old man and woman nodded their heads. "All right, child," they said. "No matter what happens, we will not look behind the screen while you are weaving."

Soon, they could hear the sound of the girl working at the loom. "Click-clack ... click-clack ... swish ... clickety-clack ..." The young girl worked from morning till night, hardly taking time to eat her meals, and all day the sound of the loom filled the little house. For three days she worked behind the screen, and finally, on the night of the third day, she brought out a beautiful piece of cloth.

"Look, Ojii-san and Obaa-san," she said, holding up the cloth, "this is what I have been weaving behind the screen."

The old man and woman took the cloth beneath the lamp so they could see it more clearly. It was a beautiful piece of **brocade** with silver and white birds flying everywhere, their wings flecked with sunlight. The two old people stroked the cloth with their hands and gasped at the loveliness of it.

....

brocade a silk fabric having raised patterns

"It is beautiful!" they said over and over again.

"Will you take it to the village tomorrow and sell it for me?" the young girl asked the old man.

"Why, of course, of course," the old man answered, "although it seems almost too beautiful to sell to anyone."

"Never mind," the young girl said. "I want you to buy me more thread with the money you get for it, and I will soon weave you another one even more beautiful."

And so, early the next morning, the old man carried the piece of brocade to the village. "Brocade for sale!" he called, as he walked down the street. "I have a beautiful piece of brocade for sale!"

Just then, the wealthy lord who lived at the top of the hill was riding through the streets. He stopped the chair in which he was riding and leaned out the window.

"Say there, old man," he called. "Let's see the brocade you have for sale."

The old man unfolded the piece of cloth and held it up for the lord to see. The great lord stroked his chin and looked at it carefully.

"Hmmmm," he said. "This is the finest piece of brocade I have seen in a long time. It glistens like a thousand snowflakes in the sun." Then he took out a bag full of gold and handed it to the old man. "Take this," he said. "Your piece of brocade is sold."

The old man hurried home with more thread and all sorts of wonderful presents and good things to eat.

"Look what I've brought home," he called happily, and he emptied all the gold coins still left in the sack. "What a happy day for us," he said, and he told the young girl how the lord had marveled over her beautiful cloth.

The very next morning, the young girl again went behind the screen and began to weave another piece of cloth. For three days the house was filled with the sound of the loom, and again, on the night of the third day, she finished another piece of brocade. The next morning, the old man went to the village and searched out the wealthy lord who lived at the top of the hill.

"I have another piece of brocade," the old man said, spreading out the second piece the girl had woven.

The lord looked at it carefully and exclaimed, "Why, this is even more beautiful than the last one." And without a moment's delay, he handed the old man an even bigger bag of gold.

The old man hurried home, laden with thread and gifts, and again they celebrated their good fortune with all kinds of good things to eat.

When the young girl went behind the screen for the third time to weave still another piece of brocade, the old woman could bear it no longer.

"I must take one little peek to see how she weaves that beautiful cloth," she said, and she got up to look behind the screen.

"But we promised," the old man warned. "We told her we wouldn't look, no matter what happened."

But the old woman wouldn't listen. "Just one look won't hurt," she said, and she stole silently to the corner of the room and looked behind the screen.

She could hardly believe her eyes when she looked, for instead of the young girl she expected to see, she saw a great white stork standing before the loom. It was plucking its own soft white feathers and weaving them into the cloth with its long beak. The old woman saw that the bird had already plucked more than half of its feathers to make the beautiful white cloth.

"Ojii-san! Ojii-san!" she cried, running back to the old man, and she told him what she had seen behind the screen.

The old man shook his head sadly. "I told you not to look," he said. And the two old people sat silently, wondering about the strange sight the old woman had seen.

That night, the young girl came out from behind the screen carrying another beautiful piece of brocade. She sat before the old man and woman and bowed low.

"Thank you for being so good and kind to me," she said. "I am the stork the old man once saved in the snowstorm. Do you remember how you freed me from the trap?" she asked.

The old man nodded and the girl went on. "I wanted to repay you for saving my life, and so I decided to become a young girl and bring good fortune to your lives. But now I can no longer stay, for this morning Obaa-san saw me in my true form, and now you know my **disguise**."

The old woman hung her head. "Please forgive me," she murmured. "I was so anxious to see how you wove your cloth, I broke my promise to you and am very much ashamed."

"Please don't leave," the old man begged, but the young girl shook her head.

"I cannot stay," she said. "But I leave knowing that you will never be poor or hungry again. Good-bye, dear Ojii-san and Obaa-san."

Then she stepped outside and became once more a beautiful white bird. Glistening in the moonlight, she spread her wings out wide and flew high into the sky. Then, circling three times over the old man and woman, she soared off toward the stars and disappeared over the hills.

....

disguise a costume or mask to hide true character or identity

The old man and woman were lonely without the sweet young girl they had grown to love, but they remembered her always. And just as she had said, they were never poor or hungry again, and lived happily and comfortably ever after.

THE GRATEFUL STORK

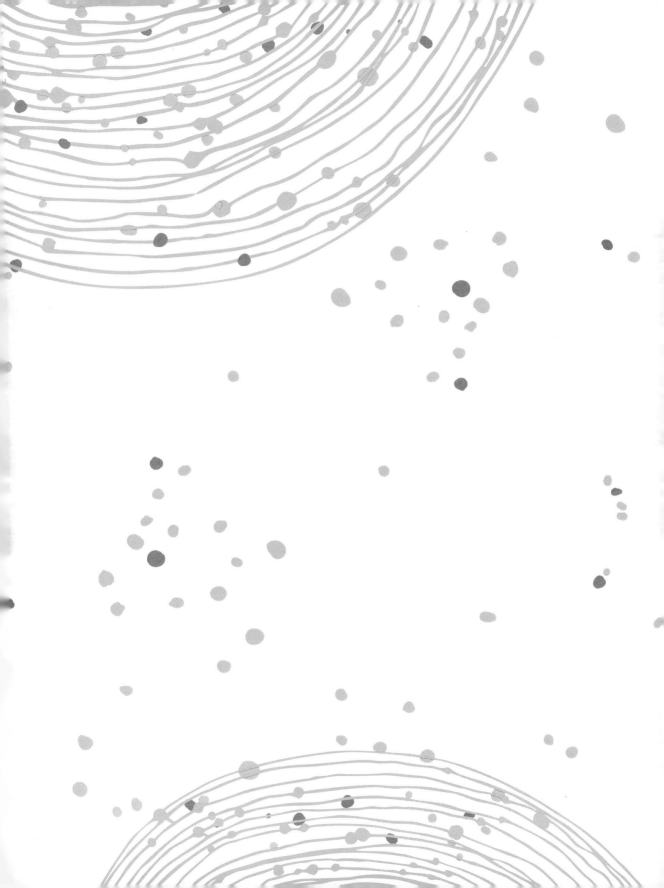

Text Credits